HOLT
ENVIRONMENTAL SCIENCE

LABORATORY GUIDE
TEACHER'S EDITION

This book was printed with soy-based ink on acid-free recycled content paper, containing 10% POSTCONSUMER WASTE.

HOLT, RINEHART AND WINSTON
Harcourt Brace & Company

Austin • New York • Orlando • Atlanta • San Francisco • Boston • Dallas • Toronto • London

CONTRIBUTORS

WRITERS

Robert Avakian
Trinity School
Midland, Texas

Kimberly Berg
Salado High School
Salado, Texas

Rainy Day
Geographer
Austin, Texas

Lynn Diebolt-Lewis
Olivet High School
Olivet, Michigan

Patricia Doran
Rondout Valley
 Jr. High School
Accord, New York

Jim Dunlap
Living Materials Center
Plano Independent School
 District
Plano, Texas

Richard Filson
Edison High School
Stockton, California

Claudia Fowler
University Laboratory School
Baton Rouge, Louisiana

Natalie Goldstein
Ithaca, New York

Stephanie Lanoue
Lago Vista High School
Lago Vista, Texas

Michael Lubich
Mapletown High School
Greensboro, Pennsylvania

Wendy Lym
Science Writer
Denver, Colorado

Patricia Merkord
Austin High School
Austin, Texas

Alyson Mike
Radley Middle School
Helena, Montana

Bruce Mulkey
Austin, Texas

Gabriell DeBear Paye
West Roxbury High School
Jamaica Plain, Massachusetts

Carol Quay
Heritage Conservancy
Doylestown, Pennsylvania

William M. Quay
Radnor School District
Wayne, Pennsylvania

Marie Ratliff
Austin, Texas

Sandra Tauer
Derby Middle School
Derby, Kansas

Carol Wagner
Pflugerville High School
Pflugerville, Texas

Ruth Willey
Fremont Ross High School
Fremont, Ohio

REVIEWERS

Margaret A. Brumsted
Dartmouth High School
Dartmouth, Massachusetts

Lynette Celano
St. Gregory Catholic School
Phoenix, Arizona

Anthony Eagan
Cajon High School
San Bernadino, California

Joseph Fontaine
Ecologist
Tehachapi, California

Susan Haskew
Texas Natural Resource
 Conservation Commission
Austin, Texas

Janis Lariviere
Westlake High School
Alternative Learning Center
Austin, Texas

Sheila Lightbourne
Choctawhatchee
 High School
Fort Walton Beach, Florida

Barbara Pietrucha
Neptune Middle School
Neptune, New Jersey

Marie Rediess
Algonac High School
Algonac, Michigan

Denice Sandefur
Nucla High School
Nucla, Colorado

Eva Silverfine, M.Sc.
Ecologist
San Marcos, Texas

Mark Stallings
Gilmer High School
Ellijay, Georgia

John M. Trimble
Corona Del Sol High School
Tempe, Arizona

Carol Wagner
Pflugerville High School
Pflugerville, Texas

Paul W. Wilson
Owasso High School
Owasso, Oklahoma

Requests for permission to make copies of any part of the work should be mailed to the following address: Permissions Department, Holt, Rinehart and Winston, 1120 South Capital of Texas Highway, Austin, Texas 78746-6487:

Photography Credits
Front Cover: water testing, Tom Stewart/The Stock Market; erosion, Carr Clifton/Minden Picutres; Ganges delta, World Perspectives/Tony Sone Images; ferns; Pat O'Hara/Tony Stone Images; cheetah, Jeff Hunter/Image Bank; clouds, Robert Stahl/Tony Stone Images; windmills, Lester Lefkowitz/The Stock Market; lungs, Photo Researchers, Inc.; contour plowing, D. Wigget/Natural Selection; sunflower, Jim Brandenburg/Minden Pictures; highways, Jose Fuste Raga/The Stock Market

Back Cover:
Pat O'Hara/Tony Stone Images

Title Page:
Jim Brandenburg/Minden Pictures

Art Credits
All art, unless otherwise noted, by Holt, Rinehart & Winston
Page 7, Thomas Kennedy; 8, Thomas Kennedy; 15, Thomas Kennedy; 16, Thomas Kennedy; 25, Leslie Kell; 28, Thomas Kennedy; 30, Thomas Kennedy; 42, Leslie Kell.

Printed in the United States of America

ISBN 0-03-053843-2

 5 6 862 03 02 01

TO THE TEACHER

The *Holt Environmental Science Laboratory Guide* is designed to introduce students to the experimental side of environmental science. As students perform laboratory investigations, they will develop their process skills and learn to apply them to environmental problems. This practical, hands-on science framework supports and extends the conceptual learning that students gain by studying the text material.

There are two basic kinds of activities in this manual:

- **Laboratory experiments** that stress hands-on laboratory skills and scientific methods

- **Issue-oriented classroom activities** that require students to think critically about environmental problems

Answers to the Investigation questions are overprinted in blue for your reference. Teaching tips appear in blue in the margins. The Investigations require only common materials and equipment that are readily available to secondary science teachers.

In addition to the Investigations, the *Holt Environmental Science Laboratory Guide* includes the following resources to facilitate instruction:

- A list of environmental organizations that students can contact

- Worksheets that accompany the Investigations found in the *Holt Environmental Science* student text

- Laboratory safety information

- Instructions on collecting and organizing scientific data

- A master materials list

Participation in the Investigations offered in this manual will promote higher levels of understanding and appreciation for the environment. Use it and enjoy!

LABORATORY GUIDE

CONTENTS

Investigation Pacing Guide			
Investigation	**Time required**	**Investigation**	**Time required**
1.1	2 periods	8.1	1 period
1.2	1 period	9.1	1 period
2.1	1 period	9.2	1 period
2.2	1 period	9.3	12 consecutive periods
3.1	2 periods	10.1	2 nonconsecutive periods
3.2	1 period	10.2	1 period
3.3	7 nonconsecutive periods	11.1	1 period
4.1	12 consecutive periods	11.2	1 period
4.2	1 period	11.3	1 period
4.3	1 period	12.1	7 nonconsecutive periods
5.1	6 consecutive periods	12.2	1 period
5.2	1 period	12.3	2 periods
6.1	1 period	13.1	11 periods
6.2	1 period	13.2	1 period
7.1	1 period	13.3	1 period
7.2	1 period	13.4	1 period
7.3	1 period	14.1	1 period

ABOUT SAFETY

Laboratory experiments are great aids to learning environmental science. However, they can involve hazards. To protect yourself and ensure the safety of others, use the safety practices described below and on the following pages.

SAFETY SYMBOLS

The following safety symbols indicate particular hazards that you may encounter while performing Investigations. You should learn what each symbol means and what precautions you should take.

 Wear approved chemical safety goggles. Wear goggles when working with a chemical or solution, when heating substances, or when using any mechanical device.

 Wear a laboratory apron or laboratory coat. Wear a laboratory apron or coat to prevent chemicals or chemical solutions from contacting skin or street clothes.

 Wear gloves. Wear gloves when working with chemicals, stains, or wild (unknown) plants or animals.

 Sharp/pointed object. Use extreme care with all sharp instruments such as scalpels, sharp probes, and knives. Do not cut objects while holding them in your hand; always place them on a suitable work surface. Never use double-edged razors in the laboratory.

 Electrical hazard. To avoid electric shock, never use equipment with frayed cords. Tape electrical cords to work surfaces to ensure that equipment cannot fall from a table. Also, never use electrical equipment around water or with wet hands or clothing. When disconnecting an electrical cord from an outlet, grasp the plug rather than the cord.

 Dangerous chemical/poison. Always wear appropriate protective equipment, including eye goggles, gloves, and a laboratory apron, when working with hazardous chemicals. Never taste, touch, or smell any substance, and never bring it close to your eyes unless specifically instructed to do so by your teacher. Never return unused chemicals to their original containers. Do not mix any chemicals unless your teacher tells you to do so. Also, never pour water into a strong acid or base because this may produce heat and spattering. Instead, add the acid or base slowly to water. If you get any acid or base on your skin, flush the area with water and contact your teacher right away. Finally, report any chemical spill to your teacher immediately.

Flame/heat. Whenever possible, use a hot plate for heating rather than a laboratory burner. Use test-tube holders, tongs, or heavy gloves to handle hot items. Do not put your hands or face over any boiling liquid. When heating chemicals, be sure the containers are made of heat-proof glass. Also, never point a heated test tube or other container at anyone. Be sure to turn off a heat source when you are finished using it.

 Glassware. Inspect glassware before use; never use chipped or cracked glassware. Do not attempt to insert glass tubing into a rubber stopper without specific instructions from your teacher. Clean up broken glass by using tongs and a brush and dustpan. Discard the pieces in a container labeled "sharps."

 Plants. Do not ingest any plant part used in the laboratory, especially seeds. Do not rub any sap or plant juice on your skin, eyes, or mucous membranes. Wear disposable polyethylene gloves when handling any wild plant. Wash hands thoroughly after handling any plant part. Avoid the smoke of burning plants. Finally, do not pick wildflowers or other plants unless instructed to do so by your teacher.

 Live animals. Do not touch or approach any animal in the wild. Always get your teacher's permission before bringing any animal into the school building. Handle animals only as your teacher directs. Always treat animals carefully and with respect.

 Biohazard. Wear appropriate personal protection, including disposable neoprene gloves and other gear provided by your teacher. Clean your work area with disinfectant before you begin and after you complete the Investigation. Do not touch your face or rub your skin, eyes, or mucous membranes. Wash your hands thoroughly after use. Dispose of materials as instructed by your teacher.

LABORATORY SAFETY

When working in the laboratory, always follow the safety guidelines described in detail on pages 425–428 of your *Holt Environmental Science* textbook. Those safety guidelines are summarized here.

While in the laboratory, at all times . . .

be prepared. Read any Investigation thoroughly before attempting to do it. Know the locations of emergency equipment, and learn how to use it. Also, be sure that you know how to perform the emergency procedures for fire, chemical exposure, etc. that are found on pages 426–427 of your textbook.

stay organized. Keep your work area neat. Bring to class only books and other materials that are needed to conduct an Investigation.

do not proceed without supervision. Never perform any experiment that has not been specifically assigned by your teacher. And never work alone in the laboratory.

wear the right protective clothing. Wear close-toed shoes to protect your feet from accidental spills or dropped equipment. Tie back long hair, roll up loose sleeves, and put on any personal protective equipment required by your teacher.

watch for safety symbols. Be alert to the meaning of all safety symbols used in this book. Know how to respond to each symbol.

report any accident, incident, or hazard to your teacher immediately. Even if such an incident seems trivial, be sure to report it right away. Any incident involving bleeding, burns, fainting, chemical exposure, or ingestion should also be reported to your school nurse or school physician.

do not eat or drink, and do not apply cosmetics. Never store food in the laboratory. Wash your hands at the conclusion of each laboratory Investigation and before leaving the laboratory.

treat laboratory animals and plants cautiously and with respect. Always follow your teacher's directions for the proper care of live specimens. Remember to protect the safety of laboratory animals and plants as well as your own safety when you work with them.

clean your work area. When you have finished your work, follow your teacher's directions for cleanup and disposal of all laboratory materials.

ORGANIZING DATA

Data are records of facts and findings obtained from an Investigation. The type of data collected depends on the Investigation. For example, it may be a set of notes made during laboratory measurements; or even diagrams, drawings, or photographs. No matter which type of data it is, it must be collected, recorded, and analyzed carefully to ensure accurate results.

To collect good data, start by gathering all necessary equipment. Usually, you will want a clipboard with paper, a pencil, and any data sheets provided in the description of the Investigation.

When recording data, there are several important practices to keep in mind. First, always label your data appropriately. Labeling ensures that your experimental findings can be easily understood by you or anyone else. One important kind of labeling involves measurements. When making measurements, *always* record the units you are using. A measurement of "5" is incomplete; "5 cm" is much clearer. Another general rule is to record *all* your data. Even if data appear to be wrong, they are important. Discoveries are sometimes made by analyzing apparent inconsistencies in data. Most often, data that seem to be "wrong" are the result of experimental error; so if you obtain suspicious data, record them and then check to see that you are doing the experiment properly.

DATA TABLES

Data tables are probably the most common means of recording data. Prepared data tables are sometimes available in laboratory manuals, but it is important that you be able to construct your own. One way to do this is to choose a title for your data table and then make a list of the types of data to be collected. This list will become the headings for your data columns. For example, if you collected data on plant growth that included both the length of time it took for the plant to grow and the amount of growth, you could record your data in a table like the one shown in **Figure A.** Note that the units of measurement are provided in the column headings. Make all data tables you will need before running your experiment and starting to gather your data.

Figure A

Plant Growth Data	
Time (days)	Height of plant (cm)
1	10
3	12
5	15
7	18
9	20

GRAPHS

After you have recorded your laboratory data, you must determine how to display it. A table may serve this purpose, but graphs are sometimes better. Graphs represent information in a pictorial form that can often be interpreted "at a glance." Two types of graphs that are commonly used are the line graph and the bar graph.

Line Graphs

In a line graph, the data are arranged so that variables are represented as a single point. A straight line is then drawn through all of the data points. For example, the line graph shown in **Figure B** is easily constructed from the data in the plant growth table. The first step is to draw and label the axes. The horizontal axis usually represents the *independent variable*. The independent variable is the variable whose values are chosen by the experimenter. In the plant growth experiment, time is the independent variable. The vertical axis of a line graph is usually reserved for the *dependent variable*. The dependent variable has values that are determined by the independent variable. In the line graph below, the height of the plant depends on time, so plant height is the dependent variable.

Next, you must choose a scale for each of the axes. Choose the scales so that the graph takes up as much of the paper as possible because large graphs are much easier to read than small ones. The scales should feature wide intervals that are evenly spaced. Be sure to label the axes with the variables plotted. For example, notice how the axes have been labeled in **Figure B.**

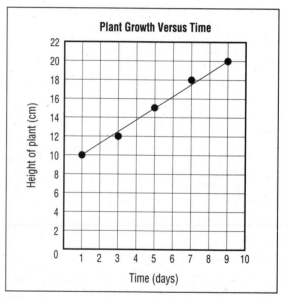

Figure B

After the axes have been drawn, scaled, and labeled, the data points are plotted. To plot each data point, lightly draw a horizontal line from the value on the vertical axis extending into the graph. Then draw a vertical line from the value on the horizontal axis extending into the graph. Where these two lines intersect, mark the data point. Once all the data points are drawn, draw the line that best fits through them. Remember that you do not "connect the dots" when you draw a line graph; instead, you draw the line between them that is as close to the points as possible. This best-fit line may not include every point in the data, but you should ensure that the average distance from the points to the line is as small as possible.

Finally give your line graph a brief title. Usually, the title should say how the variables are related to one another.

Bar Graphs

Bar graphs, or *histograms,* are convenient visual aids for comparing values of the same category. A bar graph is shown in **Figure C.** This graph compares the amount of water consumed for various purposes each day in the United States. The first steps in making a bar graph are similar to those for the line graph. You must choose your axes and label them. The independent variable remains on the horizontal axis, and the dependent variable is on the vertical axis. However, instead of plotting points on the graph, represent values of the dependent variable as a bar. Finally, title your bar graph.

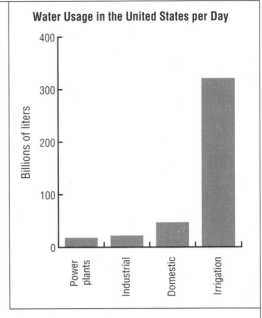

Figure C

DIAGRAMS

If your data are not numerical, they cannot be put into a table or graphed. Frequently, the best way to represent this type of information is to draw and label it. To do this, simply draw what you see, including all the features that you think are important, and then label as many parts or structures as possible. This technique is especially useful when conducting observations. For example, if you were interested in recording the foot adaptations of birds you observe in a wetlands habitat, you could diagram them as shown in **Figure D** below.

There are several things to remember as you make your diagrams or scientific drawings.

1. Make drawings large enough to be easily studied.
2. Drawings should show the spacing between parts of the specimen in proportion to its actual appearance. Size relationships are important in understanding and interpreting observations.
3. Label your drawings clearly and neatly. Lines drawn from labels to corresponding parts should be straight, so be sure to use a ruler. Label lines should never cross each other.
4. Be sure to title all drawings. Someone who looks at your drawings should be able to identify the specimen. Remember, neatness and accuracy are the most important parts of any diagram—you don't have to be an artist to make useful scientific drawings.

Figure D

Coot (lobed swimming foot)   Mallard (webbed swimming foot)   Jacana (wading foot)

INVESTIGATION 1.1

SCIENTIFIC INVESTIGATIONS

The job of a scientist is to observe and explain the natural world. Many observations do not have an obvious explanation, so scientists generate hypotheses, or potential explanations, and test them with experiments.

A good scientist considers all the factors that might be responsible for what he or she observes. Factors that can vary and that we can measure are called *variables*. Examples of variables include temperature, time, water level, number of organisms, and so on. We can investigate the role of a specific variable by keeping all other variables constant while changing the variable we are testing and then observing what happens. This process is called a *controlled experiment*. For example, we might hypothesize that fish swim slowly at night because the water becomes cool. In a controlled experiment, we would examine the swimming speed of fish at different temperatures. The variable that we change, in this case water temperature, is called the *independent variable*. The variable that we think is affected by the independent variable, in this case swimming speed, is called the *dependent variable*. We could also hypothesize that fish swim more slowly at night because it's dark, and we would then examine the influence of light level (an independent variable) on swim speed (the dependent variable).

THINK ABOUT IT

1. Why don't scientists try to test many variables in a single experiment?

   Answers will vary; answers should consider the confusion that could arise from

   relating more than one independent variable to several dependent variables.

WRITING HYPOTHESES

Hypotheses are critical to scientific investigation because they form the bases of our experimental design. Writing good hypotheses can be trickier than you think. We can make a number of statements about fish swimming speed that can be interpreted in different ways by changing just a few words. For example, consider the following:

- Fish swam slowly last night.

- Cold temperatures caused fish to swim slowly last night.

- Fish swimming speed is influenced by temperature: at cool nighttime temperatures they swim more slowly than at warmer daytime temperatures.

Each statement includes references to fish swim speed and temperature. However, each statement has its own meaning and only one can be considered a hypothesis. The first is not a hypothesis because rather than stating an explanation, it simply states two facts: (1) fish swam slowly and (2) it was nighttime.

MATERIALS

- solution of yeast, corn syrup, and water
- 3 large test tubes (20 mm × 200 mm)
- #2 one-hole stoppers (3)
- 3 rubber or plastic delivery tubes
- 400 mL beakers (3)
- 100 mL beakers (3)
- ice cubes
- thermometer
- clock
- graph paper

This lab can be a 2-day activity; the first day should focus on the mechanics of writing hypotheses, while the second day should be used to complete the lab and reinforce the purpose of hypotheses by testing a hypothesis that a student has written.

The second is also not a hypothesis because although it is an explanation about what happened (fish swam slowly *because* it was cool); it states this explanation as an indisputable fact and is therefore not **testable.** Only the last statement is a hypothesis. It proposes an explanation for the swim speed of fish at night (temperatures are cooler), and it is testable because we can put fish in water of different temperatures and observe their swim speed.

A good hypothesis clearly states what variable we want to test and predicts its effect. It is not important if your hypothesis turns out to be right or wrong. What matters is that you can test it and draw an appropriate conclusion based on your data.

CONVERTING QUESTIONS TO HYPOTHESES

Below are some questions about the environment. Read them, and identify what variables can be controlled (independent) and what variables will be observed (dependent). Rewrite each question as a hypothesis. Double-underline the independent variable, and single underline the dependent variable. Your hypothesis should clearly state the predicted response of the dependent variable when the independent variable is manipulated. The independent variable can be increased, decreased, or even removed during the experiment.

For example, the question, "Is the rate at which a substances gains or loses heat related to its density?" can be restated as the hypothesis, "The more dense a substance is, the faster it will gain heat." Other possibilities are equally valid (for example, "the more dense a substance is, the more slowly it will gain heat," etc.)

2. Question: How does the amount of energy that hits the Earth in the form of light rays relate to the angle at which those rays strike (latitude)?

   Hypothesis: Less energy is transferred to the Earth by light rays that strike at smaller angles.

3. Question: Does rainfall influence the distribution of different biomes such as deserts, grasslands, and forests?

   Hypothesis: Rainfall plays a major role in determining the distribution of different biomes.

4. Question: Does the extinction of a predator species result in a faster rate of population growth in the prey species?

   Hypothesis: The extinction of a predator species allows for more rapid population growth in the prey species.

5. Question: Is plant cover related to soil erosion?

   Hypothesis: Plant cover helps prevent soil erosion.

PUTTING HYPOTHESES TO WORK

Let's investigate a scientific question by making a hypothesis and conducting an experiment that tests your hypothesis. Yeast is a common microorganism that plays an important role in making bread. Yeast obtains energy to live by converting sugar to alcohol and carbon dioxide in a process called *fermentation*. According to a bread recipe, you dissolve a package of yeast in warm water and add flour, corn syrup, salt, and oil. The bread dough is kneaded several times and then left in a warm place to rise before being baked in a hot oven.

6. The question of interest is, "What does temperature have to do with fermentation by yeast?" Restate this question as a hypothesis.

Increasing the temperature of the yeast's environment causes an increase in the rate

of fermentation (carbon dioxide release).

EXPERIMENT DESIGN AND PROCEDURE

Your team will set up three test tubes containing yeast, water, and corn syrup stoppered with a gas-delivery tube. By placing the end of the delivery tube underwater, you can count the gas bubbles given off by the yeast. Each test tube of yeast will be in a water bath of different temperature. Tube A will be in a water bath cooled by a few ice cubes, tube B will be in room-temperature water, and tube C will be in a warm water bath.

7. Assemble the apparatus, and allow it to sit for 5 minutes so that the air pressure has time to stabilize. After the 5 minute pause, place the open end of the delivery tube underwater and begin to collect data on gas production. For the next 10 minutes keep count of the number of gas bubbles released from each tube, and record your counts in the table below.

8. Prepare a graph of the data using time on the *x*-axis and the total of gas bubbles released on the *y*-axis. Plot three curves on the same graph and label each with the temperature you recorded for each test tube. Compare your graph with that of at least one other team before handing in your report.

Carbon Dioxide Bubbles Released by Yeast										
Time (min.)	1	2	3	4	5	6	7	8	9	10
Tube A: ____ °C										
Tube B: ____ °C										
Tube C: ____ °C										

For every six teams, mix 1 tbsp. of dry active yeast, 1 L of warm water, and 200 mL of corn syrup. Combine the ingredients 15–20 minutes before each class. Note that sugar will be provided in corn syrup.

Teams of 3 or 4 work well in this activity.

Test tubes should be filled about halfway. Using temperatures around 4–10°, 20–25°, and 40–45°C will provide good results.

INTERPRETATIONS AND CONCLUSIONS

9. Which set of conditions is most similar to the conditions for the bread dough in the recipe? Why were two other conditions used in this experiment?

The warm-water test tube is most similar to conditions for the bread dough because the recipe calls for the dough to be placed in a warm place to rise. The other two conditions were controls to be sure that the yeast produced less gas under cooler conditions.

10. Why should you compare your results with those of other teams before writing your conclusion?

Comparing your results with those of other teams makes sure that the results are reliable and that the experiment is repeatable. The more replication that exists, the more reliable the results are.

11. What was the independent variable in this experiment? Why?

The independent variable was temperature because it could be controlled.

12. What was the dependent variable in this experiment? Why?

The dependent variable was the presense of gas bubbles because they were what was observed.

13. Write a conclusion for this experiment. Describe how the independent and dependent variables are related. Tell how the data supports this conclusion.

Fermentation is affected by temperature. The rate of fermentation increases when the temperature increases. The amount of gas produced was highest in the warmest test tube.

14. What does temperature have to do with making bread dough rise?

Dough rises faster at warm temperatures because gas from fermentation is released more quickly.

15. Science is not just something you know but also something you do. Explain this statement in light of what you have learned in this investigation.

Science is making observations, asking questions, seeking solutions to problems, writing hypotheses, and testing the variables through controlled experiments.

Discuss with students the distinction between reliability and validity. In science, *reliability* means the repeatability of experimental results. If you get the same results every time you perform an experiment, you know the results are reliable. *Validity* refers to the objective accuracy of your experimental results. Results are valid if they correctly illustrate the relationship you are testing. For example, say you observe that the sun rises just after your alarm clock rings and you hypothesize that your clock alarm is responsible for the sun rising each morning. You then test your hypothesis by observing the correlation between the timing of your clock alarm and the sunrise over the course of a week. If your alarm is set to ring just before sunrise, you will indeed find that the results of your experiment are reliable. However, your results do not provide a validation of your hypothesis or experimental design. The results are not valid because even though your alarm may ring just before sunrise, the rising of the sun has no objective relationship to the timing of your clock alarm.

INVESTIGATION

1.2

THE SECRET OF THE SCIENTIFIC METHOD

The scientific method can seem like something strange and mysterious—a special ritual used by people in white lab coats. But here is the secret behind the scientific method: It's really just a method of problem solving based on everyday life. You have been using the scientific method without even knowing it.

The steps of the scientific method include:

- observing and doing background research
- hypothesizing and predicting
- experimenting
- organizing and interpreting data
- forming a conclusion

Let's look in on a normal morning at the Hectic household. Tom Hectic is leaving for school, or at least trying to. The clock is showing 8:05 A.M., only 15 minutes before the tardy bell rings at Tom's school. As he frantically searches in his pockets and backpack Tom exclaims, "I can't find my house key! I can't leave without it! I'll get detention until I graduate! Mom, have you seen my key anywhere?"

"No, dear," comes his mother's calm reply.

"It's got to be in the pocket of the jeans I wore yesterday. Have you washed the clothes yet?" Tom shouts to his mother.

After getting another no for an answer, Tom sprints to his room and starts rummaging through a pile of dirty clothes. After looking in the pockets of the jeans in the pile, Tom still can't find his key. Then he wonders if the jeans he wore yesterday might be in the laundry room, so goes there, collects all the jeans, and searches the pockets of each pair.

"*Aaaargh!*" Tom yells in frustration. "It's not here. Maybe I left it in the key jar by the front door."

TOM'S SCIENTIFIC METHOD

1. What is Tom's initial observation, and what question or problem does it address?

His initial observation is that his key is lost. It addresses the problem of lacking a

means of transportation to school.

The purpose of this exercise is twofold: to demystify the scientific method and to connect it to the students' knowledge base. Even mundane tasks, like deciding what to eat or where to go for lunch, follow the outline of the scientific method. After this activity, students should be able to see how almost any question or problem can be addressed using the scientific method.

Teaching suggestions: This activity can be extended by dramatization. This will help students who are strongly visual learners. You may also wish to assign groups of students one question to analyze. Each group can then report their findings to the class. This will allow you to match the complexity of the question to the talents of the group members.

INVESTIGATION 1.2, CONTINUED

Discussion question:
If a study or field of investigation uses the scientific method, is it necessarily a science? Ask students to justify their opinions.

2. What background research does Tom do regarding his initial observation?

Tom asks his mother if she has seen the key.

3. What hypothesis does Tom make to explain his observation? How do we know that this is a hypothesis and not a conclusion?

"Its got to be in the pocket of the jeans I wore yesterday" is the hypothesis. It is a hypothesis because it predicts the answer to his question, "Where are my keys?" and because it can be tested by searching the dirty clothes.

4. Describe Tom's experiment. Does it look like what you usually think of as a scientific experiment?

Looking for the keys is Tom's experiment. It does not look like a normal experiment because it is not being done in a lab by a scientist.

5. How does Tom organize his data?

Tom organizes his data by gathering all the jeans together, which decreases the chances of overlooking a pair.

6. After Tom completes his experiment, what conclusion does he reach?

Tom concludes that his key is not in the dirty clothes. In other words, his hypothesis is wrong (refuted).

7. What does Tom do next? Do you think that scientists do the same thing when their experiments do not confirm their hypotheses? Why?

When Tom realizes that his hypothesis is wrong, he makes a new hypothesis that explains his observations, including those gathered during his first "experiment." A good scientist also revisits the scientific method, even if his or her experiment does not yield the desired results. The scientific method allows the scientist to systematically rule out various possible explanations for what he or she observes. Wrong guesses (refuted hypotheses) are useful because they narrow the field of possibilities.

Extension:
Ask students to write a story illustrating the use of the scientific method to solve a nonscience question. You may want to suggest to students that they create a mystery or detective story that is solved using the scientific method.

INVESTIGATION 2.1

IT TAKES GUTS!

Animals that eat grasses and wood really have guts—huge, industrial-strength guts! A large *gut*, which is another word for intestinal tract, is helpful for digesting cellulose, the main component of fibrous plants. Like starch, cellulose is a long chain of glucose (sugar) molecules linked together by chemical bonds. While most kinds of organisms can digest starch, only a few can digest cellulose. Why? The glucose molecules in starch all face one direction, while the glucose molecules in cellulose alternate in opposite directions. Organisms that can break the molecular bond responsible for the alternating arrangement can access the energy stored in cellulose. Such organisms include some species of fungi, protists, and bacteria.

You have probably heard of the wood-eating insects known as termites. Although termites eat wood, they cannot digest cellulose by themselves. So they get help from an amazing community of microorganisms that live in their gut. This arrangement is good for both parties: termites chew up the wood and deliver it to the microbes in their gut; the microbes in turn extract energy from the wood and supply some of it back to the termites. If a termite's microbial helpers were removed or killed, the termite would eventually starve because it could no longer obtain energy from its food. In this Investigation you will extract and observe some of the diverse microbes that live in a termite's gut.

MATERIALS

- live termites
- microscope
- slides
- coverslips
- tweezers
- saline solution
- petroleum jelly
- latex gloves

Termites can be gathered from decaying logs and woodpiles. Exterminator or entomologists at local research institutions or extension offices may be able to direct you to places where you are most likely to find termites. Termites may also be ordered from biological supply companies.

Inform students that it is not necessary to kill termites in this procedure. The termites may be be gently squeezed to induce them to evacuate a portion of their intestines.

Termite   **Cross section of termite and guts**

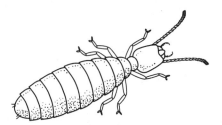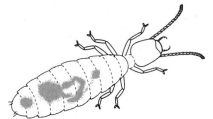

PROCEDURE

1. Place a drop of saline solution on a slide.

2. Use a pair of tweezers to pick up a termite and hold its hindquarters in the drop of saline. Gently squeeze the termite with the tweezers. This will induce the termite to excrete a small amount of intestinal fluid into the saline. Replace the termite in its container.

3. Rub a small amount of petroleum jelly on a piece of paper. Scrape all four edges of a coverslip over the petroleum jelly so that a small amount lines the outer edge of the coverslip. Place the coverslip over the drop of saline, and gently press out visible air bubbles. This procedure makes an airtight seal around the slide. This keeps the microorganisms on the slide alive because they are anaerobic, meaning that they need an oxygen-free environment to live.

Name_____ Class_____ Date_____

A good reference for termite biology is a chapter called "The Termites" in E. O. Wilson's book *The Insect Societies* (Belknap Press, Cambridge MA, 1971; pp. 103–119).

4. Observe the gut contents under the microscope, moving from low power to high power and back again. How many different kinds of microorganisms can you see?

Students should be able to see at least two different kinds of organisms.

5. In the space below, draw pictures of at least two different kinds of microorganism that you observe on the slide.

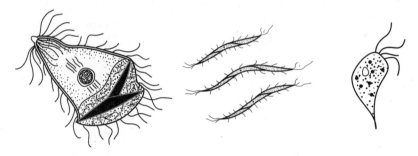

6. How do you think each of the organisms that you drew moves around?

Many use cilia, and some use flagella. The amoeboids will "ooze" their way around.

7. What do you call the kind of relationship between the termite and its microbes? Who benefits from this relationship, and how?

mutualistic; the termite benefits by getting energy from cellulose, and the microbes

benefit by getting a supply of cellulose delivered to them.

8. What might happen if microorganisms similar to the ones in the termite also lived in your gut?

I could digest cellulose and could therefore obtain energy from food sources such as

trees, hay, and paper.

9. What might the effect of different environments (chemicals, gases, temperature) have on the microbes? How could you find out?

Different environments might harm or even kill the microbes in the termite's gut. I

could find out by removing microbes from a termite's gut and trying to grow them

under different environmental conditions.

INVESTIGATION 2.2

MISBEHAVING MEALWORMS?

Behavior is the way an animal acts. Observing the responses of an animal to various cues or stimuli tells us a great deal about the animal's behavior. For example, if a lizard perches on twigs in its terrarium, it is reasonable to guess that it is an arboreal lizard and that it therefore naturally spends much of its life perched in the branches of bushes or trees.

In this Investigation you will study the behavior of mealworms. Despite their name and appearance, mealworms are not worms; they are the larval stage of grain beetles. Adult grain beetles are black and shiny, but as larvae they look like small armored worms.

You will manipulate the environment of mealworms in various ways and observe the reactions of the mealworms. You will then use your observations to better understand the natural behavior of these larvae.

SET THE STAGE

1. First create a circular arena in which to observe the mealworms' behavior. Use scissors to cut a sheet of plain white paper to fit the bottom of a dissecting pan. Tape the sheet into the pan, making sure that all edges are taped down, so the mealworms can't crawl under the paper. Trace a circle around the bottom of a 150 mL beaker in the center of the paper. Why is it important to draw a behavioral arena?

   <u>**The behavioral arena will help standardize our experiment because it ensures that**</u>

   <u>**each mealworm encounters the same experimental conditions.**</u>

SOME LIKE IT DARK

2. Fit a piece of aluminum foil tightly across the top of one half of the dissecting pan. Arrange the pan so that the uncovered side is well lighted but the covered side is as dark as possible. You can do this easier if you have a desk lamp with an adjustable beam.

3. Fold an index card in half lengthwise and then open it up so that it can be used as a scoop. With a small paintbrush carefully brush 10 mealworms onto the card and transfer them to a 150 mL beaker. Pour them all at once into the circle at the bottom of your pan. Arrange the mealworms around the outer edge of the circle, and space them apart as evenly as possible. Observe the mealworms for 5–10 minutes.

MATERIALS

- mealworms
- dissecting pan
- 150 mL beaker
- cornflakes
- bran flakes
- sweet cereal
- white paper
- aluminum foil
- transparent tape
- scissors
- small paintbrush
- index card
- desk lamp with an adjustable beam (optional)

Groups of 2–4 work best for this activity.

Tell students that animal behavior is often a response to stimuli in the animal's environment. Insect behavior is almost completely instinctual, which means that insects react in set, often predictable, ways to a given stimulus. A behavioral arena allows an investigator to provide stimuli in a controlled environment and therefore determine the insect's typical behavioral responses.

INVESTIGATION 2.2, CONTINUED

Tell students that many of the mealworms' behaviors are adaptations. Like physical adaptations, behavioral adaptations help organisms survive and reproduce in their natural environment.

4. How many mealworms moved into the lighted area? into the shaded area? What light conditions appear to be preferred by the mealworms?

   The mealworms will probably have moved to the dark side of the pan.

5. Are the mealworms bunched up or spread out? Where in the pan did they end up?

   Mealworms generally prefer to huddle together in dark corners.

LET THEM EAT FLAKES

6. Transfer the mealworms back to the beaker, and remove the aluminum foil. Make four piles of material (one pile each of white paper pieces, bran flakes, cornflakes, and sweet cereal) at equally spaced points around the circle. Which pile do you think the mealworms will prefer? Why?

   The mealworms will move toward the pile (behavioral response) of the best food

   source (stimulus). This behavior is an example of an instinct.

7. Brush one mealworm at a time into the circle. Observe each mealworm for one minute before adding another. Record how many mealworms visit each pile. Also make a note if a mealworm does not visit any pile for a full minute.

8. Once all the mealworms are in the tray, observe their activity for 10 minutes and, continue to record their visits to the piles.

Discuss the nature of the mealworms' relationship with their food source, grain. Ask students if the relationship can be described by one of the terms on pages 39–42 of the textbook. Tell them that this is an example of a predator-prey relationship. Notice that it differs from common ideas of what a predator-prey relationship is. The lesson students should learn is that predators and prey do not always play cat-and-mouse.

Food Preferences of Mealworms		
Location	**Initial tally**	**Final tally**
Bran flakes	_____	_____
Cornflakes	_____	_____
Sweet cereal	_____	_____
Paper	_____	_____
No pile	_____	_____

9. Which pile was most preferred by the mealworms?

   Mealworms normally prefer cereal to paper, and cornflakes are a big favorite.

10. How do you think mealworms' behavior helps them survive?

    Mealworms' preference for dark places leads them to food sources they can burrow

    into, such as piles of stored grain, where they can also hide them from predators.

I N V E S T I G A T I O N

3.1

DISSECTING OWL PELLETS

Owls are not known as finicky eaters. They prey on almost any animal that is small enough to be swallowed whole. Like many other birds, owls have an interesting adaptation: a special structure that prevents the indigestible parts of their prey—fur, feathers, bones, and so on—from passing into their intestines. These indigestible parts are shunted to a storage pouch, where they accumulate. A few hours after consuming a meal, the owl coughs up the accumulated indigestible material, which has been compressed into a pellet. Examining such a pellet can tell you what the owl ate. An examination of the remains of the owl's prey can give you a good idea of what the prey ate. Using this information, you can construct a simple food chain of the owl's environment.

THE TELLTALE PELLET

1. Working in groups of three or four, examine an owl pellet. Separate the fur or feathers from the bones. Identify the major components of the pellet.

2. If the pellet contains remains from more than one organism, determine as best as you can how many animals and species are present.

3. Attempt to group the remains by organism. Then try to assemble complete skeletons. Sample skeletal diagrams are shown below.

4. Closely examine the skulls of the prey animals. Compare them to the diagrams of skulls on the next page. To what purpose do the teeth or bills seem most suited—tearing flesh, chewing plant parts, or grinding seeds? If you are able to identify the prey animals, find out their usual food sources.

MATERIALS

- owl pellet
- dissecting tools (such as toothpicks or tweezers)
- disposable gloves
- egg cartons
- small animal identification field guide with skull illustrations

Groups of 3 or 4 students work well for this activity.

Provide latex gloves for students who are squeamish about handling the owl pellets. Remind students not to eat or drink during the activity and to wash their hands thoroughly afterward.

This lab requires patience and careful handling of the smaller bones. Caution students to work carefully as the bones may be brittle and sharp. Encourage students to use tweezers rather than their fingers to gently pick apart the pellets.

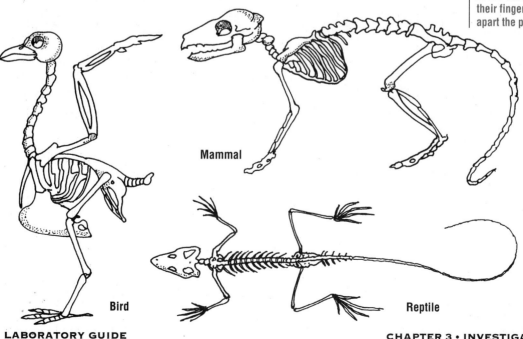

Mammal

Bird

Reptile

INVESTIGATION 3.1, CONTINUED

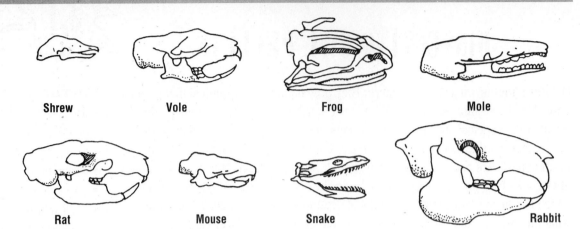

Shrew	Vole	Frog	Mole

Rat	Mouse	Snake	Rabbit

Suggest that students sort the bones first by shape and then by size. Student groups may find egg cartons useful for sorting and classification. Label each compartment to hold bones of similar type, such as skull, femur, or vertebrae. Students should not assume that the bones are those of adult animals.

Students may make a poster to display their food chains.

5. On a separate piece of paper, construct a simple food chain based on your findings.

6. Compare your findings with those of other students.

ANALYZE YOUR FINDINGS

7. What kinds of animals did you identify in the owl pellet?

Students are likely to find the remains of a variety of small animals, such as lizards,

snakes, mice, rats, shrews, moles, voles, and young squirrels or rabbits.

_____

_____

8. Compare your findings with those of your classmates using the following questions:

a. What animals were represented most often in the pellets?

Answers will vary.

_____

b. What common traits do these animals have?

Answers will vary but may mention small size, nocturnal activity, and so on.

_____

9. What biological relationships were you able to determine from your examination of the owl pellets?

Answers will vary but may mention that owls feed on different types of animals that

are either primary or secondary consumers. Students may also observe that a

predator-prey relationship exists between the owl and the animals on which it feeds.

Sample food chain:

```
            Owl
         /       \
      Mouse      Vole
     /    \      /    \
  Seeds Insects Seeds Bulbs
```

INVESTIGATION 3.2

THE CARBON CYCLE

Carbon, a chemical element, is a component of nearly all biological molecules. Carbon is found in all organisms, where it is one of the main components of cells. Organisms get energy from carbon compounds. Organisms obtain carbon from their environment. Plants get carbon through photosynthesis, while animals get carbon by eating plants or by eating organisms that ate plants. Think of the food you eat—it mostly consists of parts or products of living organisms. Consider a slice of pizza. The crust is made from wheat, which is part of a plant; the sauce is made from tomatoes, the fruit of a different plant; and the cheese is made from milk, an animal product. All of these animal and plant products supply you with the carbon compounds you need to live and grow.

So what do organisms do with carbon compounds? Through a process called *cellular respiration,* the cells of most organisms use oxygen to release the energy that is stored in food molecules. Fungi use a different process, called *fermentation,* that does not use oxygen to release energy. During both cellular respiration and fermentation, energy is released when the chemical bonds that hold the food molecules together are broken. All organisms then use elements, such as carbon, to build their own biological molecules. The molecules left after these processes are waste products.

One of the waste products is carbon dioxide, a molecule that contains carbon. As organisms conduct cellular respiration or fermentation, they release waste carbon dioxide as a gas into the atmosphere. Photosynthetic organisms, such as plants, absorb this carbon dioxide and use it in photosynthesis. The carbon gets incorporated into parts of the plant (for example, as part of the starch in a potato) and may end up being consumed by yet another animal. The constant cycling of carbon through organisms to the atmosphere and back again is called the *carbon cycle.*

MATERIALS

- bakers yeast (check expiration date)
- 0.5 g sugar
- warm water
- 0.5 g salt
- 50 mL beakers (3)
- 100 mL beaker

THINK ABOUT IT

1. What kinds of organisms use carbon in the creation of cells?

All organisms use carbon in the creation of cells.

2. What happens to the carbon you eat but do not use in the creation of cells?

It is released back into the atmosphere as a gas.

PROBLEM

In this experiment you will be working with yeast, a single-celled organism that is a fungus. Yeast obtains energy from food through the process of fermentation. By providing the yeast with different sources of food, we will answer the following question: What substance is used by yeast as a source of energy?

Groups of 3 or 4 students work best for this activity.

PROCEDURE

3. To prepare a yeast solution, add 1 g of dry baker's yeast to 100 mL of very warm water, and stir the mixture gently.

4. Label three beakers 1, 2, and 3, and fill each half full with yeast solution.

5. Dissolve 0.5 g of sugar in beaker 2 and 0.5 g of salt in beaker 3.

6. Note what happens in each beaker, and record your observations in the data table. Be sure to look for bubbles rising to form a foamy layer. **This is evidence of carbon dioxide production.** Be sure to use your sense of smell also!

Reaction of Yeast to Different Food Sources	
Beaker	**Observations**
1	The water and yeast form a clumpy, cloudy mixture that has an unpleasant smell. There is no change in the mixture over time.
2	Bubbles start to form and make a foamy layer on top of the mixture.
3	The cloudy mixture does not have any bubbles. It has an unpleasant smell.

ANALYZE YOUR OBSERVATIONS

7. Which beaker served as the control in this experiment?

beaker 1, yeast solution without food source

8. What food sources were tested in this experiment?

sugar and salt

Compare this equation to the equations for photosynthesis and cellular respiration on page 58 of the textbook.

Below are the word and chemical equations for the fermentation carried out by yeast cells.

$$\text{sugar} \xrightarrow{\text{enzymes}} \text{energy} + \text{alcohol} + \text{carbon dioxide}$$

$$C_6H_{12}O_6 \xrightarrow{\text{enzymes}} \text{energy} + 2C_2H_5OH + 2CO_2$$

9. Did you notice a smell of alcohol in any beaker, and if so, which one? What does this mean?

beaker 2; fermentation is occurring with alcohol as a byproduct

INVESTIGATION 3.2, CONTINUED

10. In which of the beakers did you notice bubbling, and what does this mean?

2, again fermentation is happening; CO_2 is being produced

11. Based on the equations on the previous page and on what you observed, in which of the beakers do you think the process of fermentation occurred?

2

12. Why didn't fermentation happen in all of the beakers?

Because there was no food source in beakers 1 and 3. Water and salt do not provide

energy to living things.

13. What would you conclude is the source of the carbon in the carbon dioxide produced?

The carbon is from the glucose.

The glucose in the sugar (food source) contains the carbon resulting from photosynthesis. The carbon is returned to the atmosphere because it is incorporated into the sugar and then released back into the atmosphere by yeast during fermentation.

14. Below is a diagram that shows the path of carbon in the carbon cycle. Fill in the blanks to describe what is happening during each of the steps.

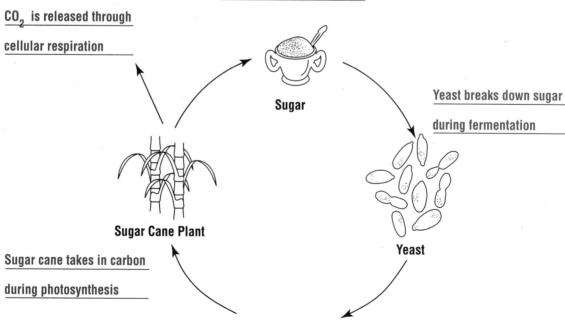

Sugar in cane is processed

into refined sugar

CO_2 is released through

cellular respiration

Sugar

Yeast breaks down sugar

during fermentation

Sugar Cane Plant

Yeast

Sugar cane takes in carbon

during photosynthesis

Carbon is released into

atmosphere as CO_2

15. Think about a sugar-based food that you commonly eat, such as bread. When you eat it, how do you become a part of the cycle we see on the last page? In the space provided below, draw another diagram of the carbon cycle in which you are one of the organisms involved. Describe what is happening at each step.

Answers will vary but should reflect the structure of the carbon cycle.

16. How is burning gas in a car similar to digestion in living organisms?

Both ot these processes liberate energy from carbon-based fuels by combining the

fuels with oxygen. Oxidation is actually a more controlled form of burning. The fuels

combine with oxygen, breaking the bonds that hold the fuel molecules together and

releasing energy that can be used to build bodies and to run cars.

17. Sugar acts as a fuel for living organisms. Gasoline, which comes from the remains of dead plants, provides the fuel for cars. Why is there so much stored energy in these fuels?

Plants take energy from the sun and convert it into high energy bonds in glucose

molecules. Fossil fuels, such as gasoline, come from the remains of dead plant

matter. Both sugars and gasoline contain this stored energy in their chemical bonds.

INVESTIGATION 3.3

A SUCCESSION OF MICROBES

In natural communities, the replacement of species that occurs over time is called succession. It may be caused by several different factors, including competition, changing resources, or one species creating resources for species that follow. The newer species thrive and may dominate the community, but they are eventually replaced by still other species until a stable climax community forms. Succession is especially noticeable after natural disasters or severe disturbances caused by humans.

In this Investigation you will study succession in two communities of microscopic organisms living in wet soil. You will place each of your communities in a Winogradsky column, a device that was originally developed by Russian microbiologist Sergei N. Winogradsky in the 1880s. You will add various nutrients to one of the columns. The other column will be your control, and you will not add anything to it. By comparing the experimental Winogradsky column with the control, you will study the effects of added nutrients on microbial succession.

BUILD WINOGRADSKY COLUMNS

1. Remove any hard lumps, twigs, rocks, and other large particles from about 1,000 cu. cm of soil. Strain soil through a sieve to remove any remaining large particles. Separate the soil into two equal piles.

2. Add a small handful of well-shredded newspaper, half of a crushed eggshell, and about one-quarter of the crumbled yolk from a hard-boiled egg to one of the piles of soil. The newspaper, eggshell, and egg yolk provide organic material, calcium carbonate, and sulfate, respectively, for various microbial populations. Mix the nutrients thoroughly with the soil.

3. Label the two plastic bottles. Label one as the control and the other as the experimental bottle.

4. Using the funnel, gently pour the soil that contains added nutrients into the experimental bottle to a height of about 5 cm. Then gently pour the soil without added nutrients into the control bottle. Use the dowel to pack the soil into the bottom of each bottle and to remove the air trapped in the soil. Add a little more soil and a few spoonfuls of pond water to each bottle, using the dowel again to pack the soil and release any trapped air. Repeat this process until the level of the soil is about 5 cm from the top of each bottle. Add water up to about 2 cm from the top of each bottle, and cap the bottles tightly.

5. Place your Winogradsky columns in an area where they will receive indirect sunlight over the next six weeks.

WATCH WHAT HAPPENS

6. Make colored sketches of the columns and their contents once a week for 6 weeks in the table on the next page.

MATERIALS

- 500 mL clear plastic soda bottles with screw-on caps (2)
- 1,000 cu. cm soil from a natural area
- sieve
- dowel (for packing the soil in the bottles)
- funnel
- spoon
- fresh water from a naturally occurring source (such as a pond)
- small handful of shredded newspaper
- one-half eggshell, crushed
- one-quarter crumbled hard-boiled egg yolk
- metric ruler
- colored pencils
- wax pencil

Groups of 2 to 4 students work well for this activity.

As a variation, you may wish to have different student groups prepare bottles with different ingredients (one with just newspaper, another with newspaper and egg yolk, etc.)

Sketches of Winogradsky Columns

Week	1	2	3	4	5	6
Control column						
Experimental column						

INVESTIGATION 3.3, CONTINUED

ANALYSIS

7. Use the following key to describe the succession in microbe populations that you observed in the experimental bottle over the course of the 6 weeks.

> **Green clumps:** algae
>
> **Black spots:** sulfate-reducing bacteria
>
> **Reddish purple spots:** purple sulfur bacteria
>
> **Rust-colored areas:** purple nonsulfur bacteria

Also describe evidence of any other populations you may have observed.

Answers may vary, but the following general pattern is typical. In 3 to 15 days, green

clumps of algae will appear. In 6 to 21 days, black spots of hydrogen sulfide (H_2S)

will be formed by sulfate-reducing bacteria and will eventually turn the entire bottle

black. In 2 to 3 weeks, purple nonsulfur bacteria will form a rust-colored zone in the

upper third of the bottle. In 3 to 6 weeks, reddish purple spots will appear near the

bottom of the bottle (indicating purple sulfur bacteria).

_____

_____

8. What differences did you observe between the two columns in terms of the rate and pattern of succession?

In general, the control column will exhibit slower and less dramatic changes.

_____

_____

_____

_____

_____

_____

_____

Sulfate- or sulfur-reducing bacteria are anaerobic. They use elemental sulfur and the sulfur in sulfates as electron acceptors to produce hydrogen sulfide (H_2S). Because they produce millions of tons of H_2S every year, they have great ecological importance. Purple sulfur bacteria use light energy to break H_2S into elemental hydrogen and sulfur, and purple nonsulfur bacteria use organic materials, such as carbohydrates, for the photosynthetic reduction of carbon dioxide.

For best results, have each group gather soil and water from a different source. This will reduce the possibility of a contaminated sample inhibiting the succession of microbes.

INVESTIGATION 3.3, CONTINUED

9. A simple sulfur cycle is going on inside the columns. The sulfate-reducing bacteria produce a substance called hydrogen sulfide (the black spots), which is used by the purple sulfur bacteria for photosynthesis. The purple sulfur bacteria then produce other forms of sulfur, which are used by the sulfate-reducing bacteria.

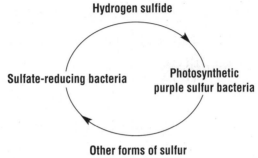

Given this information, what could you do to stop this sulfur cycle?

Removing the light energy would stop the process of photosynthesis among the

purple sulfur bacteria.

10. What could have caused the succession in your bottle, and how is it different from the succession in a natural ecosystem?

As different nutrients became more available, different populations of microbes

could thrive (such as the purple sulfur bacteria that use the H_2S produced by the

sulfate-reducing bacteria). This happens in natural ecosystems as well, but in

nature, species can arrive from outside areas (unlike in the bottle, which is a closed

system).

EXTENSIONS

You may want to try these variations and observe their effects on microbial succession in your Winogradsky columns.

- Add various pollutants (such as fertilizer or insecticide) to your column.
- Keep your column on ice or next to a heating vent.
- Expose your column to different intensities of light (direct sunlight, total darkness, etc.).
- Use different combinations of soil and water from various sources.
- Use different sources of nutrients, such as sawdust, fruit and vegetable peels, or crushed seashells.

INVESTIGATION 4.1

CLIMATIC ADAPTATIONS

The plant and animal species living in a biome adapt to their climate. In turn they modify the climate through their participation living in each biome in the water cycle. The climate of each biome varies, and the plants and animals living in each biome must be able to tolerate this variation to survive. For example, deer living in a high-altitude forest must be able to survive the dry summer as well as the cold winter.

Some biomes have more variable climates than others, so you might assume that species from the more variable biomes can tolerate larger differences in temperature and precipitation than species from the less variable biomes. Is this assumption correct? Do plants from different climates respond differently to climate? In this experiment you will explore one climatic variable: temperature. So turn up the heat, and let's get growing.

HYPOTHESIZE

1. Read the experimental design below, and identify the independent and dependent variables. Think about how they might be related and what might happen when the independent variable is changed. Write a hypothesis that expresses your prediction.

   Example: Seeds from plants native to temperate climates will germinate under a

   wider range of temperatures than seeds from native tropical plants.

DESIGN AN EXPERIMENT

2. Obtain seeds from at least two plant species that prefer warm environments and at least two plant species that prefer cool environments. Some suggestions for warm weather species include watermelon, pumpkin, cucumber, and squash. Varieties that prefer cool weather include lettuce, celery, spinach, endive, radish, beet, turnip, and parsnip.

3. Set up a series of germination tests for each variety. Line 12 Petri dishes (plastic or glass with lids) with two or three sheets of wet filter paper.

4. Place 10 seeds of each selected variety to its own dish, and label the dishes accordingly. One will be kept in an incubator at 42°C, another will be kept at 22°C (room temperature), and the third dish will be kept in a refrigerator for 16 hours per day and at room temperature for 8 hours per day.

5. Seal all dishes together in a sealable plastic bag to prevent drying out and keep the dishes at their prescribed temperatures over the next 10 days. Observe daily.

MATERIALS
- 12 Petri dishes
- various seeds
- filter paper
- sealable plastic bags
- incubator
- refrigerator
- marking pens

This is a complicated hypothesis that students may need help with. Use it as a basis for discussion.

Local availability and season will influence your choice of seeds. Germination times are usually printed on the back of commercial seed packs. These are usually between 7 and 14 days in areas where the temperature rises and falls daily. Germination at ideal constant conditions is always faster. Radishes, for example, are supposed to take 5–10 days to germinate, but at room temperature germination occurs in 24–48 hours. The temperatures given are suggested. Keeping a refrigerator at exactly 6°C might be difficult, but some variation will not affect the results.

6. Record the number of seeds that sprout roots and shoots in the data table below. Note which (root or shoot) emerges first and how many emerge. Also note if any seeds die or become infected with mold. After 10 days, combine all class data, and proceed to the analysis portion of this experiment.

Seed Germination Success			
Cool-weather seeds	Alternating cool/ warm temps. 6° to 22°C	Warm temp. 22°C	Hot temp. 42°C
Warm-weather seeds			

ANALYSIS & CONCLUSIONS

7. Which seed varieties performed best in the cool environment?

   Answers will vary but will usually include the cool-weather seeds.

8. Which seed varieties performed best in the warm environment?

   Answers will vary but will usually include the warm-weather seeds.

9. Which seed varieties germinated in the widest temperature range?

   Answers will vary, but the cool-weather seeds usually do best overall.

10. Which environment allowed the most seeds to germinate?

    Answers will vary, but the room-temperature environment is most likely.

11. Which seeds would do well in a tropical climate?

    The warm-weather seeds would do best.

12. Does temperature affect the germination of seeds? Explain.

    Yes, answers should reflect on the supporting data.

    _____

    _____

    _____

INVESTIGATION 4.2

FACTORS THAT INFLUENCE ECOSYSTEMS

Ecosystems are collections of plant and animal communities living in a specific set of environmental conditions. These conditions play an important role in determining what plants can live there. Because animals depend directly and indirectly on plants to live, the existence of certain plants partly determines what animals can live there. The Earth's major ecosystems, such as deserts, tropical rain forests, and taiga, are called *biomes.*

In the previous activity you learned that latitude has a strong influence on an area's temperature, resulting in polar, tropical, and temperate climates. However, a careful look at a map reveals that ecosystems at the same latitude often have different climates. Why? This activity will point you toward the answer.

MATERIALS

- transect grid
- ruler

Start by discussing the concepts of ecosystems and biomes. List the factors that can influence ecosystems across different continents. Develop the idea that rainfall and altitude are independent of latitude, while temperature is not. Make a key on the graph that identifies the two line graphs. You may also find it useful to label the location names.

THINK AHEAD

1. What factors account for differences in ecosystems found at the same latitude? Suggest some possible environmental factors that vary across the United States from San Francisco to Washington, D.C.

   Rainfall and altitude will be the most common answers. Some students may suggest

   temperature and humidity as well.

PROCEDURE

In this procedure you will test two hypotheses, one that relates differences in ecosystem vegetation to rainfall and another that relates differences in ecosystem vegetation to altitude. Complete the following sentences to form your two hypotheses.

Students can work individually or in pairs for this activity.

2. Ecosystem distribution is related to precipitation; regions that receive a lot of precipitation are wet and therefore

   support ecosystems with more vegetation.

3. Ecosystem distribution is related to altitude; regions at higher altitudes are cold and therefore

   support ecosystems with little vegetation.

Look at the data table on the next page. The table lists major cities and weather stations between the latitudes 36°N and 41°N. It also lists the altitude, average annual precipitation, and ecosystem in each location. Plot altitude on the transect grid provided on page 25, and connect the points. Use the *y*-axis on the left side for your altitude scale. Plot the precipitation data on the same grid, connecting the points and using the scale on the right. You may also find it useful to label the location names. Your completed line graph will help you see any relationship between rainfall, altitude, and biome type.

Characteristics of Locations Across the U.S.			
	Distance from San Francisco	Altitude above sea level	Average rainfall in./yr.	Natural biome or ecosystem
San Francisco, CA	0	250'	23"	redwood forest
Sacramento, CA	100 mi.	26'	19"	grassland
Donner Pass, CA	200 mi.	7,000'	69"	coniferous forest
Reno, NV	250 mi.	4,400'	8"	cool desert
Salt Lake City, UT	650 mi.	4,200'	16"	cool desert
Loveland Pass, CO	900 mi.	11,000'	38"	coniferous forest
Denver, CO	950 mi.	5,325'	12"	short grass prairie
Topeka, KS	1,450 mi.	925'	34"	tall grass prairie
St. Louis, MO	1,750 mi.	567'	37"	broadleaf forest
Cincinnati, OH	2,100 mi.	488'	40"	broadleaf forest
Washington, DC	2,500 mi.	9'	39"	broadleaf forest

ANALYSIS

4. Is there a definite trend in precipitation levels from Denver to San Francisco or from Denver to Washington, D.C.? If so, describe it.

Yes, there is a trend from Denver to Washington, D.C. Rainfall increases as you

travel toward the Atlantic Coast. Mountains interrupt the trend to San Francisco.

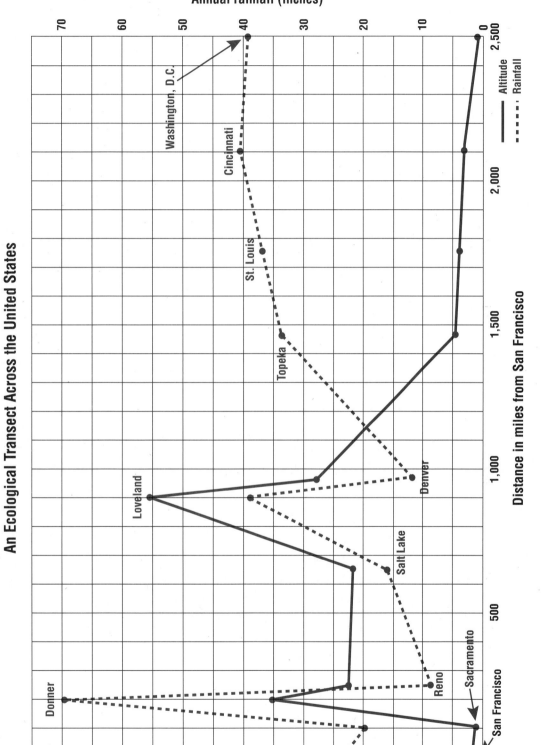

An Ecological Transect Across the United States

5. How do mountain ranges affect precipitation? Give an example that supports your answer.

Rainfall increases on the leeward side of mountain ranges. Donner and Loveland

passes are good examples of this effect. Locations following mountains always have

lower rainfall.

6. What kinds of ecosystems occur in areas of high and low precipitation?

Forests are more common in high-rainfall areas, and deserts are more common in

low-rainfall areas.

7. Is precipitation level or altitude the more important factor in determining an area's ecosystem? Is there an interaction between these two factors? Explain.

Both factors are very important. Higher altitudes tend to have forest ecosystems

(Donner Pass), unless there is not enough rainfall, in which case the area is a high

desert (Salt Lake City).

8. Does the data support or refute your hypotheses about the effect of precipitation and altitude on an ecosystem type?

The data support my hypothesis that precipitation nurtures ecosystems with lush

vegetation. The data does not clearly support or refute my hypothesis that increasing

altitude negatively affects vegetation.

9. Refer to the world biome map (Figure 4-1) on page 79 in your textbook, and examine the ecosystem patterns of the Eurasian continent. What do you infer about the distribution of rainfall in Eurasia?

Eurasia's ecosystems tend to have temperate deciduous forest near its east and west

coasts. As you travel to the interior, forests give way to grassland and grassland

gives way to desert. This implies that rainfall decreases as you move from coastal

areas to interior areas.

INVESTIGATION 4.3

A MATTER OF DEGREE

Consider the following familiar observations: (1) In areas with temperate climates, as in most of the United States, daily temperatures change dramatically with the seasons. (2) The position of the sun in the sky changes with the seasons. For example, in summer the sun is almost directly overhead at midday, while in winter it is closer to the horizon. (3) If you travel at least 300 mi. north or south to a different latitude, the climate changes. Areas near the equator generally have warm climates, and those near the poles generally have cool climates. How can we explain these observations? In other words, what causes the differences in temperature that accompany changes in season and changes in latitude?

FORM A HYPOTHESIS

1. The observations above suggest a relationship between the position of the sun in the sky and the average temperature of the Earth's surface. Read the experimental design below. Identify the independent and dependent variables, and use them to propose a hypothesis about the relationship between the angle of the sun's rays and the Earth's temperature.

   The closer the angle between the sun and the Earth is to 90° (i.e., the more direct the angle of the sun's rays striking the Earth), the higher the temperature at the Earth's surface is.

EXPERIMENT

2. Obtain four cereal boxes of equal size, and remove the front panel from each box.

3. Line the inside of the boxes with black paper. Then cover the open sides with clear plastic wrap, and seal the edges with tape.

4. Arrange the lamps over three of the boxes so that the bulb is approximately 6 in. from the surface. Arrange the first lamp so that the light makes a 90° angle with the bottom of the first box (as in Diagram 1). Aim the second lamp at a 45° angle. Aim the third lamp at a 22.5° angle. Do not put a lamp above the fourth box. What is the purpose of the fourth box?

   The fourth box is the control. It will let us see if the air temperature changes due to a factor other than direct exposure to light.

5. Turn on the lamps and note the temperature in each box every minute for 21 minutes. Record your data in Table 1.

MATERIALS

- 4 cereal boxes (small to medium sized)
- black paper
- clear plastic wrap
- thermometer (alcohol-type recommended)
- 3 gooseneck lamps with bulbs of 60 W or greater
- scissors
- tape
- protractor

For help with hypotheses, direct students to the lab on Scientific Investigations.

Groups of 2 to 4 students work well for this activity.

In order to save class time, you may wish to have students prepare the boxes at home the day before the lab.

Diagram 1

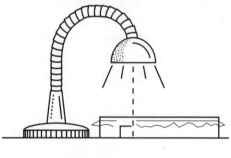

90° angle

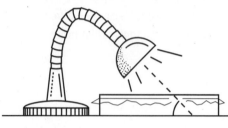

45° angle

22.5° angle

Table 1

Temperature of Boxes Heated by Lights at Different Angles											
Time in min.:	0	1	2	3	4	5	6	7	8	9	10
Temperature in °C (light at 90° angle)											
Temperature in °C (light at 45° angle)											
Temperature in °C (light at 22.5° angle)											
Temperature in °C (no light)											

Table 1 (continued)

Temperature of Boxes Heated by Lights at Different Angles											
Time in min.:	11	12	13	14	15	16	17	18	19	20	21
Temperature in °C (light at 90° angle)											
Temperature in °C (light at 45° angle)											
Temperature in °C (light at 22.5° angle)											
Temperature in °C (no light)											

6. On a piece of graphing paper, make a line graph with the data from Table 1. Use the *x*-axis to record time and the *y*-axis to record temperature. Make sure to label each line with the appropriate lamp angle.

7. In which box did the greatest change in temperature occur?

   The greatest change occurred in the box receiving the most direct light, 90°.

8. In which box did the smallest change in temperature occur?

   The least change occurred in the box with no light striking it.

9. What do the differences between the slopes of the curves for each of the angles imply about the rate of heat gain?

   The differences imply that temperature rises faster in more direct light.

10. Energy can change forms, such as when light is absorbed by an object and turned into heat, but energy cannot be lost; it must go somewhere. Since all the lamps gave off the same amount of energy, where did the energy go with respect to the boxes that never reached high temperatures?

    The energy was absorbed or reflected by surfaces other than those inside the box,

    such as the tabletop.

11. What is your conclusion about the relationship between the angle of light and the temperature?

    The more direct the angle at which light strikes a surface, the more light that is

    absorbed and turned into heat.

EXTENSION

12. How does the principle of the previous experiment apply to the Earth and its climatic zones? To demonstrate your understanding of this principle and its implications for the Earth, draw latitude lines for the Arctic Circle, the Tropic of Cancer, equator, the Tropic of Capricorn, and the Antarctic Circle on the diagram below. Label each line with its degree of latitude. Color the warmest zone yellow, and label it "Tropical Zone." Color the coolest zone blue, and label it "Polar Zone." Finally, color the remaining zone green, and label it "Temperate Zone."

■ I N V E S T I G A T I O N ■

EUTROPHICATION:
TOO MUCH OF A GOOD THING?

Plants depend on nutrients such as phosphates and nitrates to survive. However, when people release large amounts of these nutrients into rivers and lakes, artificial eutrophication can occur. In artificial eutrophication, nutrients cause algae and plant life to grow rapidly and then die off and decay. When microorganisms decompose the algae and plant matter, they use up oxygen in the water, causing the death of fish and other animals that depend on oxygen for survival. Eutrophication is commonly caused by phosphates, which are often found in detergents, and by nitrates, which are found in animal wastes and fertilizers. In this Investigation you will observe artificial eutrophication in an aquatic ecosystem.

MATERIALS
• 1 qt. jars (3)
• wax pencil
• distilled water
• fertilizer (household use)
• graduated cylinder
• stirring rod
• pond water containing viable organisms
• plastic wrap
• fluorescent lamp
• eyedropper
• microscope
• microscope slides with coverslips
• guide to pond life identification

Spirogyra
(producer)

Volvox
(producer)

Daphnia
(consumer)

Vorticella
(consumer)

Some common pond organisms

SET UP YOUR EXPERIMENT

1. Working with your team, use a wax pencil to label one jar "Control," a second jar "Fertilizer," and a third jar "Excess fertilizer."

2. Put 750 mL of distilled water in each of the three jars. Read the label on the fertilizer container to determine the recommended dilution of fertilizer for watering plants. To the "Fertilizer" jar, add the amount of fertilizer recommended for a quart of water. To the "Excess fertilizer" jar, add 10 times this amount of fertilizer. Stir the contents of each jar thoroughly to dissolve the fertilizer.

3. Obtain a sample of pond water. Stir it gently but thoroughly to ensure that the organisms in it are evenly distributed. Measure 100 mL of pond water into each of the three jars.

4. Cover each jar loosely with plastic wrap. Place all three jars about 20 cm away from a fluorescent lamp. (Do not place the jars in direct sunlight, as this may cause them to heat up too much.)

Groups of 2 or 3 students work well for this activity.

If pond water is not available, you may use water from an aquarium.

You can also create a good water sample by soaking dried grass in dechlorinated tap water for 5–7 days. This infusion will provide a variety of organisms for observation.

OBSERVE ECOSYSTEM CHANGES

As an alternative, leave tap water in a container for 24 hours to allow the chlorine to dissipate, or use a chlorine neutralizer made for aquariums. Inoculate the water with a stock algae culture, such as *Spirogyra* or *Chlorella*. This will not provide the diversity of organisms that natural pond water would provide, but it will enable students to observe algae growth.

If necessary, demonstrate how to use a microscope and prepare a slide.

5. Observe a drop of pond water under the microscope. In the space below, draw at least four of the organisms that you see. Determine whether the organisms you see are algae (usually green) or consumers (usually able to move). Describe the number and type of organisms that you see.

Answers will vary.

_____

_____

_____

6. Based on your understanding of eutrophication, make a prediction about how the pond organisms will grow in each of the three jars.

Algae will grow most abundantly in the "Excess fertilizer" jar and least in the

"Control" jar. Growth of algae in the "Fertilizer" jar will be intermediate. Eventually,

algae will begin to die and decay in all jars.

_____

7. Observe the jars when you first set them up and at least once every three days for the next 3 weeks. Note color, odor, and any visible presence of life-forms. Record your observations in the table on page 34.

8. When life-forms begin to be visible in the jars (probably after a week or two), use an eyedropper to remove a sample of organisms from each jar, and observe the sample under the microscope. How have the number and type of organisms changed? Record your observations below.

There should be an increase in the number of algae present in the two "Fertilizer"

jars. Some species may have increased in number, while others may have

decreased because the conditions in the jars were more favorable for one species

than for another. There may be a decrease in all organisms in the "Control" jar.

9. At the end of your 3-week observation period, once again remove a sample from each jar and observe it under the microscope. In the space provided, sketch at least four of the most abundant organisms and describe how the number and type of organisms have changed.

Algae probably will have further increased in number in the two "Fertilizer" jars.

However, as the algae grow and start to become overcrowded, some algae may

begin to die, especially in the "Excess fertilizer" jar.

ANALYZE YOUR RESULTS

10. After 3 weeks, which jar shows the most abundant growth of algae? What may have caused this growth?

The most abundant growth will probably be in the "Excess fertilizer" jar because the

added nutrients promoted rapid algae growth.

Extension:
Conduct the experiment using gradually larger concentrations of fertilizer such as 1×, 2×, 4×, etc. This extension will better illustrate the cycle of growth that leads to eutrophication.

11. Did you observe any effects on organisms other than algae in the jar with the most abundant algae growth? Explain.

Other organisms may increase in abundance as their food supply (algae) increases.

However, if algae have begun to die and decay, the decay process may deplete

oxygen in the jar, causing oxygen-dependent life-forms to die as well.

12. Did your observations match your predictions? Explain.

Answers will vary. One reason for a discrepancy between predictions and observa-

tions may be that conditions in the jars have not yet reached the later (die-off and

decay) phases of eutrophication.

13. How can artificial eutrophication be prevented in natural water bodies?

Students might suggest passing laws to prevent or control pollution and contamina-

tion, using better methods for purifying wastewater, or limiting fertilizer use.

Name_____ Class_____ Date_____

Control			
Date	Color	Odor	Other observations

Fertilizer			
Date	Color	Odor	Other observations

Excess fertilizer			
Date	Color	Odor	Other observations

INVESTIGATION 5.2

OPERATION OIL SPILL CLEANUP

Offshore oil drilling and the use of supertankers for transporting oil can lead to oil spills. Oil spills can damage fishing grounds, spoil beaches, kill marine birds and mammals, and destroy shellfish beds. A mere 1 gal. of oil can contaminate as much as 5 million gallons of water. Because you are concerned about these issues, you have chosen to work for Eco-Marine, Inc., an environmental remediation firm that specializes in solving ocean pollution problems. Your supervisor has distributed the following memo describing a new assignment.

MEMO

To: All Eco-Marine Staff
From: Marina Waters, President
Re: Oil Spill Cleanup Proposal

Mega Oil Company is accepting proposals for a cleanup plan that could be implemented in the event of an oil spill from one of their supertankers. There are several top-notch companies competing for this contract, so we need to work hard to show Mega that *we* can do the best job. We must develop a plan for a cleanup that is fast, effective, and minimally harmful to the environment.

Each work team will develop its own plan. First you will test cleanup materials, and then you will develop a complete cleanup plan. We will then test the plans and choose the best one to submit to Mega.

Marina Waters

MATERIALS:

- 100 mL vegetable oil
- 9 in. × 13 in. pan
- 2 shallow containers for water
- spoon
- small beaker
- sand (or gravel)
- pipe cleaners
- feathers
- watch (or clock)
- several of the following: spoons, craft sticks, toothpicks, dip nets, drinking straws, plastic wrap, aluminum foil, pieces of plastic foam, string, pieces of brown paper bag, cotton balls, pieces of nylon stocking, pieces of sponge, paper towels, coffee filters, cloth, wood shavings, sawdust, liquid detergent

Groups of 4 to 6 students work well for this activity.

Three days are recommended for the activity, as follows: (Day 1) test materials, (Day 2) develop a plan, and (Day 3) test the plan.

In preparation, students may read a magazine article about an actual oil spill, such as "A Clot in the Heart of the Earth," *Outside*, June 1989, which covers the 1989 *Exxon Valdez* spill. *The Big Spill* (NOVA video) provides an excellent summary.

TEST CLEANUP SUPPLIES

1. Work with a team of students as assigned by your teacher. From the materials list, select 5–10 supplies to use to clean up an oil spill.

2. Pour a spoonful of oil onto the surface of water in a shallow container to represent an oil spill in the open ocean. Pour a small amount of oil onto rocks, sand or gravel, pipe cleaners, and feathers in another container for testing cleanup of the shore and wildlife. (The pipe cleaners represent sea mammals, and the feathers represent birds.)

3. Test your supplies to determine their effectiveness in the following categories:

   - containing an oil spill

   - cleaning up the water and recovering spilled oil

   - cleaning up the shore and wildlife

   Also evaluate the environmental impact of using a large quantity of each of your cleaning supplies in the ocean.

Name_____ Class_____ Date_____

Record your ratings of each material in the table below. Rate each material as poor, average, good, or excellent.

Evaluation of Cleaning Supplies					
Material	**Containment**	**Water cleanup & oil recovery**	**Shore cleanup**	**Wildlife cleanup**	**Environmental impact**

DEVISE A PLAN

4. Write complete directions for cleaning up an oil spill with the supplies you tested. You must specify materials and techniques for the following:

- containment of the oil spill
- cleanup of water and recovery of oil
- shore cleanup, including both rocks and sand
- wildlife cleanup and reintroduction into habitat (include birds, shore animals, and sea animals)
- minimizing the impact of your cleanup operations on the ocean ecosystem

Library research may improve the accuracy of students' cleanup plans.

Cleanup plans will vary but should include all factors listed above.

_____

_____

_____

_____

TEST YOUR PLAN

5. Build a model ocean in a 9 in. × 13 in. pan. Create a beach using sand or gravel and a few rocks at one end of the pan. Place a feather and a pipe cleaner at the shoreline. Add water carefully.

> Adding food coloring to the water will make the oil more visible. To make the model more realistic, use a 3.5 percent saltwater solution (made by adding 35 g of salt to 965 mL of water) in place of tap water.

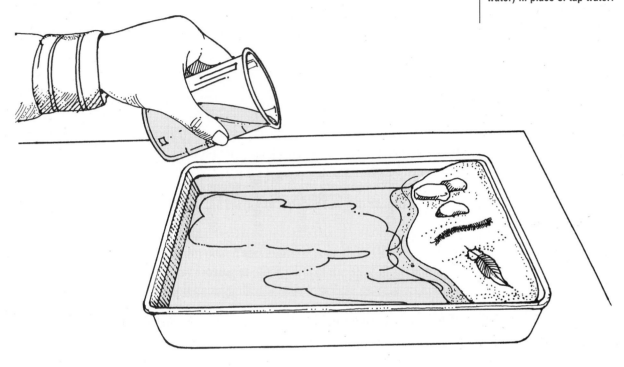

6. Let a small beaker of oil represent your supertanker. Spill 50 mL of oil into the center of your water area. Gently blow the oil toward the shore.

7. Implement your cleanup plan. Your goal is to complete the cleanup as quickly and effectively as possible. For each cleanup task (oil containment, oil recovery, shore cleanup, and wildlife cleanup), have a separate column to record the time it takes to complete the task and how well the cleanup works.

Time and effectiveness will vary._____

_____

_____

_____

_____

_____

Tell the students that this experiment is a very simplified model of a complex situation. The difference in scale makes it difficult to extrapolate the results of this lab to an actual oil spill.

TEAM DEBRIEFING

8. After all teams have finished their cleanup, present your results to the class. Take a class vote to determine whose plan should be submitted to Mega Oil Company.

9. What containment method worked best? How would weather affect the results?

Several containment methods are possible. Winds would severely complicate the

process.

_____

_____

10. Was it possible to recover any of the oil? Could the recovery methods that worked best be used in a real oil spill?

Oil could be recovered. This would be difficult but possible on a large scale.

_____

_____

_____

11. What happened when the oil reached the beach? How effective was cleanup of sand and wildlife?

Oil penetrates the sand and the fur, feathers, or skin of animals. It is extremely

difficult to remove.

_____

_____

Extension:
Calculate the approximate area of an oil slick. Drop 1 mL of motor oil (20 drops) into a dish of water. Use clean motor oil and have students wear gloves, goggles, and aprons. Collect all the oil after the experiment is finished and dispose of properly. To obtain the slick size for a spill of 11 million gallons (the amount spilled in the Valdez incident), use the following conversion factors:
1 L = 1,000 mL
1 gal. = 3.785 L
1 sq. ft. = 929 sq. cm
1 sq. mi. = 27,900,000 sq. ft.
Use a surface current map to determine where the oil might end up if this quantity of oil were spilled in an ocean near where you live.

12. What factors might make a real oil spill cleanup different from your simulation?

Winds, currents, temperature, water salinity, and the type or weight of the oil would

affect results, as would the availability of materials on a large scale.

_____

13. In a real spill, what impact might cleanup methods have on plant and animal life?

Cleanup methods that use detergents or hot, pressurized water sprays can harm

plant and animal life.

_____

_____

■ I N V E S T I G A T I O N ■ **6.1**

TESTING ACID, TRACKING RAIN

There are two forms of air pollution, particulate and gaseous. Particulate pollution consists of small solid particles, like ash and soot. These particles are carried by wind currents until they settle out, after the wind has calmed. Gaseous pollution consists of chemical gases that are vaporized during combustion and industrial processes. The gases mix with air and sometimes chemically combine to form other substances. Oxides of nitrogen, sulfur, and carbon react with water vapor to form acids. When these acidic vapors condense into liquid droplets, the result is acid rain.

Acid rain has both direct and indirect effects on organisms. Direct effects include the death of aquatic plants and animals and the injury and death of trees that take up acidic water. Indirect effects include the leaching of aluminum from soil and the death of organisms that depend on organisms directly killed by acid rain.

The major source of sulfur and nitrogen oxides is the combustion of fossil fuels, including coal burned in power plants and gasoline burned in vehicles. Because these gaseous pollutants are airborne, they can easily travel hundreds of miles from their source before combining with water. In this Investigation you will test various substances for acidity and examine how acid rain is formed and distributed.

MATERIALS

- pH paper
- dropper pipet
- variety of solutions, from acid to base
- disposable soda straw
- Erlenmeyer flask
- yeast culture
- microscope

WHAT'S YOUR pH?

1. First you will learn how to measure acidity using the pH scale. pH is a measure of the number of free hydrogen ions in a solution. Ions are atoms or groups of atoms that have a positive or negative electrical change. Solutions with a low pH have many hydrogen ions (H^+) and are called *acidic*. Solutions with a high pH have few hydrogen ions and are called *basic*. Your teacher will give you a variety of common chemical solutions. Place a drop of each solution on a fresh piece of pH paper, match the resulting color to the pH scale, and identify the pH. List the substances and their pH below.

   battery acid (HCl): pH < 1; lemon juice: pH 2; vinegar, wine, carbonated drinks, and

   acid rain: pH 3; tomato juice: pH 4; coffee and clear rain: pH 5; milk: pH 6.5; pure

   water: pH 7; sea water and egg white: pH 8; baking soda: pH 9; detergent and milk of

   magnesia: pH 10; household ammonia and washing soda: pH 12; hair remover and

   oven cleaner: pH 13; sodium hydroxide and drain cleaner: pH 14

Groups of 2 to 4 studetns work well for this activity.

Prepare a yeast culture by dissolving a package of dry active yeast into 250 mL of warm water and 25 mL of corn syrup. Prepare and mix this solution 15 minutes before class. Use a microscope to view yeast reproduction, or budding. Everyone should have the same yeast dilution as a starting point for conducting the acid dilutions.

Be sure to use pH paper that can measure a wide range of pHs.

2. How does your pH paper indicate an acid? a base? What color indicates a pH of 7?

The paper turns red in an acid, blue in a base, and yellowish-green at pH 7.

3. Which of the substances you tested are strong acids? Which are strong bases?

Answers will depend on the substances used. Lemon juice and vinegar are relatively

strong acids, and ammonia and oven cleaner are relatively strong bases.

Caution students to avoid breathing too quickly or strenuously because this can cause them to hyperventilate.

4. Did you know that you can create acid by breathing? Carbon dioxide from your breath combines with water vapor in the air to form carbonic acid, H_2CO_3, which separates into H^+ and HCO_3^- in liquid. You will need a soda straw, an Erlenmeyer flask, distilled water, and pH paper. Check the pH of the distilled water and record it in the chart below. Gently blow through the straw into the water for 10 seconds. Check and record the water's pH again. Blow for 10 more seconds and record the pH. Repeat the procedure until you have exhaled through the water for 120 seconds. Be sure to pause and rest between each 10-second interval so that you do not hyperventilate and become dizzy.

pH of Water into Which You Exhale													
Time (sec.)	0	10	20	30	40	50	60	70	80	90	100	110	120
pH													

5. Describe the change in pH in the water when you exhaled. Did this form a strong or weak acid?

Answers will vary, but should indicate that pH decreased as more air was blown.

If yeast cells are too numerous to count, you or students can do serial dilutions using a 10 mL graduated cylinder or by mixing one drop of culture with nine drops of water. Repeat this dilution five times to reach a million-to-one ratio.

6. Now you will determine how acid concentrations affect living microorganisms. First prepare a live yeast culture by placing 1 mL of the culture into 9 mL of water. Examine the yeast under a microscope to observe that the yeast cells are actively budding. Check the pH of the culture. Seven teams in your class will each add a solution of sulfuric acid, H_2SO_4, to their yeast tube, wait 10 minutes, and measure the pH. The first team will add 1 mL of 1 molar H_2SO_4 to their yeast culture. The second team will dilute the acid 10:1. The third team will dilute the acid twice, making it 100:1; the fourth team will dilute it three times, making it 1,000:1; the fifth team will dilute it four times, making it 10,000:1; the sixth team will dilute it five times, making it 100,000:1; and the seventh team will dilute it six times, making it 1,000,000:1. Record the pH values measured by each team in the table on the following page.

Response of Yeast to Increased Acidity							
	1 molar H2SO4	Diluted 10-1	Diluted 10-2	Diluted 10-3	Diluted 10-4	Diluted 10-5	Diluted 10-6
pH							
Yeast budding							

7. Describe how pH affects the microorganism yeast.

The budding activity is reduced by low pH, but the effect of the acid becomes negligible as it is diluted.

FIND THE RAIN'S FINGERPRINT

Rainwater normally has a pH of about 5.7. This is slightly more acidic than the pH of pure water, which is about 7. Acid rain has a pH of 5 or lower. By conducting pH tests and studying the distribution of acidified water bodies, you can trace acid rain to its source.

8. Using the information in the chart below, find areas with pH values of 5 or lower. Then mark these areas on the map on the following page. The prevailing winds in this area blow from west to east. Armed with this information, study the map and determine where you think the most likely source of the acid rain is, and mark the spot with an **X.** Draw an arrow on the map showing the direction that the acidic pollution travels from its source.

This section can be done during class time or assigned as homework. Discussing the solution would be an excellent lesson in critical thinking.

pH at Various Coordinates on the Map							
Coordinates	M2	U4	L8	Y10	G13	K15	S19	DD17
pH	7.4	7.2	7.3	7.3	7.3	7.0	7.1	7.1
Coordinates	Y22	EE22	N27	FF26	FF28	J22	J26	O29
pH	6.7	4.9	6.2	4.7	4.8	7.3	6.8	5.0
Coordinates	U30	BB33	K35	K39	FF38	AA41	U38	F42
pH	4.5	5.0	6.0	6.5	5.8	6.0	5.5	6.7

Teaching tip:
Discuss the natural variability of pH in rivers and lakes. Human impact causes this natural range of pH to move into the acidic range. These changes can be plotted on the map by using different colors to represent increasingly low pH levels. For consistency with the pH color scale, have students plot map points in the following colors:

red = pH 5.0 or lower
purple = pH 5.1 to 6.0
green = pH 6.1 to 7.0
blue = pH 7.1 or higher

Solution:
A basic assumption is that acid rain forms downwind from the source of pollution. Based on this assumption, the most likely source is the eastern edge of the northern-most of the two largest cities. This city shows the greatest amount of acid rain directly to its east. The acid likely originates on the eastern edge because there are no acidic deposits in the city itself and because power plants are usually located at the edges of urban areas. The river that flows through the cities is only slightly acidic due to dilution of the water from rivers from the north, which show no evidence of acid rain and are slightly basic.

Misconception alert:
Some students may misunderstand the direction of stream and river flow on the map and be inclined to point arrows away from the pollution source along the main waterways. If confusion arises, point out that water generally flows from smaller waterways into larger waterways. Therefore, acid rain production from the city is not likely to travel north by water from the metro area because that would be upstream.

Distribution of Acid Rain (pH)

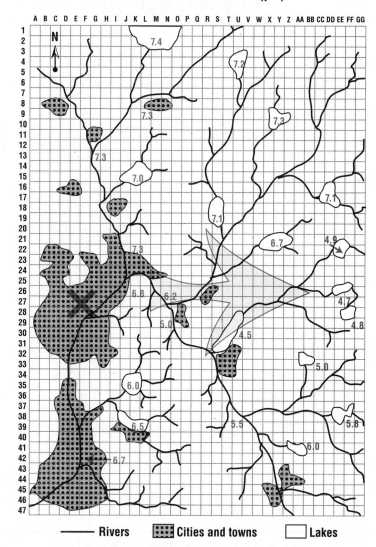

—— Rivers   ▓▓ Cities and towns   ☐ Lakes

9. Write a paragraph in which you identify the source of the air pollution and its general path through the region. Describe how you made your choice, and provide evidence to support your decision. Hint: Sulfur dioxide, the main culprit in acid rain, is produced primarily by power plants that burn fossil fuels. Sulfur dioxide mixes with air. It takes time to form sulfuric acid, so the acid rain is likely to fall some distance from the sulfur dioxide source.

Answers should vary only slightly. The source of the pollution should be within one or

both of the heavily populated areas in the southwest corner of the map. The arrows

showing where the pollution is distributed should point east. Students' reasons for

having the source of the pollution lie in the metro area(s) could include the fact that acid

rain can be caused by the emmisions of car engines, which are concentrated in the

cities, as well as by power plants, which are also more likely to be in populated areas.

I N V E S T I G A T I O N

6.2

THE ACID TEST

Acid precipitation is one of the effects of air pollution. When nitrogen- or sulfur-containing pollutants react with water vapor in clouds, dilute acids form. These acids fall to the Earth as acid precipitation.

Often, acid precipitation does not occur in the same place where the pollutants are released. The acid precipitation usually falls some distance downwind—sometimes hundreds of kilometers away. Thus, the site that causes acid precipitation may not suffer its effects. This is one of the reasons why solving the problem of acid precipitation has been so difficult.

Coal-burning power plants are one source of air pollution. These power plants release the chemical sulfur dioxide into the air. Sulfur dioxide reacts chemically with the water vapor in air to produce sulfur-containing acids, which later fall to Earth as acid precipitation.

In this Investigation you will perform a chemical reaction that produces sulfur dioxide. When this sulfur dioxide reacts with water vapor in the air, the same acids that result from coal-burning power plants form. You will observe the effects of these acids on plants.

PROCEDURE

1. Place 2 g of sodium nitrite in a beaker. Place a plant and the beaker inside the plastic bag. Do not seal the bag yet.

Caution: Steps 2–4 should be carried out ONLY under a fume hood or outdoors.

2. Carefully add 2 mL of a 1 M solution of sulfuric acid to the beaker. Immediately seal the bag tightly, and secure the seal with a twist tie or tape. *Caution: Because this reaction produces sulfur dioxide, a toxic gas, the bag should be absolutely free of leaks. If a leak occurs, move away from the bag until the reaction is complete and the gas has dissipated.*

3. Seal an identical plant in an identical bag that does not contain sodium nitrite or sulfuric acid.

4. After 10 minutes, cut both bags open. Stay at least 5 m away from the bags as the sulfur dioxide gas dissipates. Keep the plants and bags in the fume hood.

MATERIALS

- 2 g sodium nitrite
- 2 mL sulfuric acid (1 M)
- 2 potted houseplants of the same type (impatiens, marigolds, and pansies are good choices)
- 2 large, clear plastic bags
- 50 mL beaker
- twist tie or tape

Groups of 2 or 3 students work well for this activity.

When working with caustic or poisonous chemicals, use extreme caution. Allow only your most mature students to handle these materials. Alternatively, you may wish to handle the chemicals yourself or perform the procedure as a demonstration.

Test the bags beforehand for possible leaks. Use only bags that are absolutely free of leaks. Sulfur dioxide is very poisonous. Keep students at least 5 m from the simulation for the duration of the reaction.

The acidity produced by this simulation greatly exceeds what could normally occur in real life, but the effects in real life can be just as dramatic. In effect this simulation condenses months of acid precipitation into a single episode.

5. Predict the effects of the experiment on each plant over the next few days. Record your predictions.

_____

_____

6. Observe both plants over the next 3 days. Record your observations below.

Day	Control plant	Experimental plant
1		
2		
3		

ANALYZE

Invite your students to extend this Investigation by designing an experiment to test the effects of acid rain on nonliving materials, such as cars or buildings.

7. What does this experiment suggest about the effects of acid precipitation on vegetation?

The acid precipitation damages the vegetation.

8. a. In what ways is this experiment a realistic simulation of acid precipitation?

All of the basic ingredients are the same: sulfur dioxide, water, and living plants.

_____

b. In what ways is this experiment NOT a realistic simulation?

The acidity is much greater in the simulation than in real life; the length of exposure is much shorter; little or no precipitation actually forms; the simulation takes place in a sealed environment; in the simulation, the effects of exposure to acid occur more rapidly.

9. Would you expect to see similar effects occur as rapidly, more rapidly, or less rapidly in real life? Explain.

Effects would occur less rapidly in real life because the acid would be much less concentrated.

_____

INVESTIGATION 7.1

BUILD A MODEL OF GLOBAL AIR MOVEMENT

Warm air rises and cools, and cold air sinks and warms. This is true whether we are observing the temperature and air circulation in a room or around the globe. On Earth this movement of air creates a system of wind currents that you will demonstrate by building a model. You will build a closed system in which ice simulates the polar regions and a lamp simulates the equator. You will follow the movement of air over these regions by watching a trail of smoke as it traces the path of air.

SET UP YOUR GLOBAL MODEL

1. Stack the ice cubes on the bottom and against one end of the aquarium. Place the lamp outside the other end of the aquarium with the bulb directed at the bottom half of that end. Use masking tape to attach one thermometer to each end inside of the aquarium. Make sure the thermometers can be read from the outside of the tank. Place the cover on the aquarium.

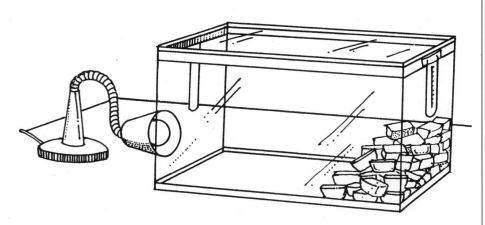

2. Wait 5 minutes; then read and record the temperature at each end of the aquarium.

_____

3. Light the end of the incense stick so that it produces a steady plume of smoke.

4. Lift the aquarium cover very slightly so that you can insert the incense stick. Hold it steadily in place over the ice about 5 cm from the cover.

MATERIALS

- 15 gal. glass aquarium with cover
- 2 outdoor thermometers
- adjustable goose-neck lamp with a 100 W incandescent bulb
- masking tape
- 24 large ice cubes
- incense stick
- matches

Groups of 2 to 4 students work well for this activity.

Alternative materials may be used in this activity. Any closed aquarium may be used as long as it is twice as long as it is deep—for example, an aquarium with dimensions of 12 in. × 12 in. × 24 in. works well. Very small tanks are not recommended. The cover can be plastic film or any material that will prevent room air currents from influencing air flow in the tank. Any lamp that is capable of directing heat in a single direction may be used. The number of ice cubes may need to be adjusted. The incense stick should be about 12 in. long. The thermometers must be hung inside each end of the aquarium.

OBSERVE AND RECORD

After two or three cycles the smoke may remain diffuse in the tank. It is important to maintain a temperature differential. Adjust the lamp periodically so that a constant temperature is maintained on the warm side of the tank. If the system becomes overwhelmed, remove the cover to clear the tank and begin again. You may need to adjust the distance of the lamp from the tank to set up the visible circulation effect.

5. How does the smoke behave? Draw a diagram of the aquarium. Use arrows to indicate the movement of the smoke.

Drawings should show that the smoke falls directly over the ice, tumbling over and down the mound of cubes. The smoke puddles at the base of the mound and then slowly begins to move and rise toward the warm end of the tank. The smoke expands and becomes diffuse as it rises at the warm end. When the smoke begins to move across the top of the tank toward the cool side, it condenses as it descends over the ice.

6. Why is the difference between temperatures at the two ends of the aquarium an important factor in the flow of heat through the aquarium?

Without a temperature differential, the air will not move. Air moves by convection.

The smaller the temperature differential, the slower the air movement.

7. Remove several ice cubes. Does the air movement pattern change when some ice is removed? Why?

Air descends more slowly because the area over the ice is warmer when some ice is

removed. Also some smoke takes a different path and does not descend at all.

APPLY WHAT YOU HAVE LEARNED

8. A *closed system* is a collection of elements that nothing can escape from or enter. Your aquarium is an example of a (practically) closed system. *Convection* is the movement of warm air relative to cooler air. Discuss your observations of convection in the closed system of the aquarium. How can you apply this information to the movement of air over the Earth?

Just as air warms and rises over the warm side of the tank, air warms and rises over

the equator. In the tank, cool air continually moves in behind the rising mass of air,

warming and rising and finally cooling and falling as it moves away from the heat

source. Similarly, warm air from the equatorial region is pushed out toward the polar

regions, where it condenses and falls. Cool air falling over polar regions will push

the mass of air below it toward the equator, where it will warm and rise, creating a

circular air flow. The air is constantly being pushed by the air behind it. In this way,

air circulation patterns are established over the Earth.

_____

_____

9. Predict how air movement patterns might change if polar ice began to thaw due to global warming.

If the polar regions were not as cold, air movement would be changed drastically, as

it was in the model when ice was removed. With a decreased temperature differen-

tial, air currents would slow and stagnate over some regions of the Earth. Rainfall

patterns would vary greatly from current patterns. For example, the equator would

probably receive more rainfall because it would be warmer and because warm air

holds more water. When warm, wet air rises and cools more rainfall is released.

Temperate climates would probably shift to the north in the Northern Hemisphere and

to the south in the Southern Hemisphere.

_____

_____

_____

Answers will be speculative. Accept all answers. Encourage thinking about how changing air circulation will affect climate and weather. These are good questions for a lively class-room discussion. See the sample answers.

INVESTIGATION 7.1, CONTINUED

10. How is the Earth and its atmosphere like the closed system of your aquarium model? What factors exist on Earth but not in your model that affect air movement, climate, and weather?

The Earth is a nearly closed system, like the model, but it is much larger and has

many more factors that influence air movement. The Earth and the model are alike

because there is a temperature difference between each end of the tank that simu-

lates the difference between the polar regions and the equator. The aquarium system

is too small to simulate the deserts and temperate zones that exist on Earth. Also

ocean currents and land masses were not simulated in the model, but they do affect

global air movement. The rotation of the Earth on its axis causes a Coriolis force to

act on air masses, further altering their pathways.

_____

_____

INVESTIGATION

7.2

METHYL BROMIDE:
THE OZONE'S ENEMY

MATERIALS
- graph paper
- colored pens or pencils

A layer of ozone is located in the stratosphere, more than 7 mi. above the Earth's surface. In section 7-4 you learned about ozone's protective function and about the chemicals called CFCs that damage this layer.

Methyl bromide, a chemical byproduct of the production of fire-retarding materials for the electronics industry, destroys the ozone layer. Methyl bromide kills organisms such as insects, nematodes, weeds, and rodents; and it causes respiratory and central nervous system problems in humans. It is commonly used as a pesticide in soil where strawberries and tomatoes are grown in Florida and California. As much as 95 percent of methyl bromide eventually enters the atmosphere, where it damages ozone.

Scientists use an index called the ozone depletion potential (ODP) to compare a substance's ability to destroy ozone. CFCs have ODPs that range from 0.1 to 1. Substances with higher numbers have more destructive potential. Methyl bromide has an ODP of 0.6. The Clean Air Act requires the phasing out of all substances with an ozone depletion potential of 0.2 or greater, including methyl bromide, by the year 2001. In addition, the Montreal Protocol, an international treaty to protect the earth's atmosphere, lists methyl bromide as a chemical concern.

Scientists claim that on a molecular level methyl bromide is 50 times more destructive to ozone than CFCs are.

Several countries, including the Netherlands, Denmark, and Sweden, have already banned the production and use of methyl bromide.

This activity works well if students work individually or in pairs.

ANALYZE THE DATA

The chart on the next page shows the level of worldwide production of methyl bromide and the changing thickness of the ozone layer between the years 1979 and 1994. The thickness of the ozone layer is measured in Dobson units. The ozone layer as it exists in the stratosphere is several kilometers thick due to the low pressure at that distance above the Earth's surface. But if you were to bring the ozone layer to the Earth's surface, the pressure would compress it to only 0.3 cm thick. To standardize comparisons of the ozone layer's thickness, the Dobson unit is defined as 0.001 atm-cm.

1. What was happening to the ozone layer in the years before methyl bromide began to be produced?

It was getting thinner.

2. Can you think of a possible explanation for the change in the thickness of the ozone layer in the years before methyl bromide was produced?

The change might have been caused by CFCs, which were being put into the atmos-

phere before the production of methyl bromide began.

Methyl Bromide and Ozone Data		
Year	Metric tons sold	Dobson units
1979	0	209
1980	0	205
1981	0	205
1982	0	189
1983	0	169
1984	100,468	154
1985	106,423	146
1986	111,233	159
1987	122,774	120
1988	133,621	173
1989	137,942	124
1990	146,923	128
1991	162,259	117
1992	157,816	124
1993	160,181	94
1994	162,547	88

GRAPH THE DATA

3. On a piece of graph paper plot the data from the chart above. Put the years on the *x*-axis and metric tons of methyl bromide sold on the *y*-axis. Label the *y*-axis in increments of 5,000. Connect these points smoothly using a best-fit line. On the same graph create a second vertical *y*-axis on the right. Label it with Dobson units with values from 80 to 200 in increments of 10. Graph the ozone layer data. Make this *y*-axis a curving best-fit line in a different color.

4. Does the increased use of methyl bromide correlate with the decrease of the ozone layer?

According to the graphed data, ozone decreased as methyl bromide use increased.

This indicates correlation. However, other factors cause ozone depletion as well.

_____

5. If there is a correlation, does that prove that methyl bromide causes ozone destruction?

Correlation is not proof. A laboratory experiment using a closed system could give

evidence concerning ozone depletion and methyl bromide use.

HOW EFFECTIVE ARE SUNSCREENS?

It's a gorgeous summer day, and you plan to spend the day swimming and soaking up some rays at a nearby park. Not wanting to suffer a painful burn, you grab a hat, spread a layer of sunscreen over your exposed skin, and put on some sunglasses before you leave.

You may know that it is the sun's ultraviolet (UV) rays that can burn you. Sunglasses and a hat provide shade for your eyes and face, but how does sunscreen help protect you?

Many sunscreens contain a chemical called para-aminobenzoic acid (PABA), which absorbs UV rays before they can be absorbed by your skin. Sunscreens use a numbered rating system. According to this system, the higher the number, the higher the concentration of PABA and the greater the UV absorption. For example, if your sunscreen has an SPF (sun protection factor) of 8, you can theoretically stay in the sun eight times longer than you could with no protection. That is, the sunscreen reduces the amount of UV radiation that your skin absorbs by a factor of 8.

Do sunscreens *really* protect us against UV radiation? Does the rating system *really* give us a way to judge the relative strength of different sunscreens? Conduct the following experiment to find out.

SUNNY SIDE UP

1. Use a wax pencil to label each acrylic sheet with the SPF rating of one of the lotions you will be testing. Include the lotion with no sunscreen.

2. Place a drop of each grade of lotion on the corresponding acrylic sheet. Using a clean cotton swab for each sample, evenly spread the lotion over the surface of each sheet.

3. Working rapidly, place a piece of sun-sensitive paper on a baking sheet with the blue side up. Arrange the acrylic sheets (lotion side up) on the paper from lowest to highest SPF. Label the paper to show the SPF of each acrylic sheet. Quickly cover the tray and sheets with dark paper to avoid exposure to light.

4. Carry the tray outside to a sunny location and uncover it, exposing it to the sun. The blue paper will fade to very light blue. This process may take up to 15 minutes, depending on solar intensity. Watch carefully as the paper fades. As soon as the paper around the acrylic sheets fades completely, cover the tray and take it back to your classroom.

5. Remove the cover and acrylic sheets from the paper. Rinse the sun-sensitive paper in cold water for one minute and spread it flat to dry.

6. Allow the sun-sensitive paper to dry, and then examine the spots where the acrylic sheets were placed.

MATERIALS

- water
- 4 sunscreen lotions with different SPF ratings
- suntan lotion containing no sunscreen (such as baby oil)
- sheet of sun-sensitive paper
- 5 small acrylic sheets, about 3 cm × 5 cm
- 5 cotton swabs
- wax pencil
- several sheets of dark construction paper or a dark cloth
- baking sheet

Groups of 2 to 3 students work well for this activity.

Sunscreens with SPF ratings of 4, 8, 15, and 30 are recommended.

Sun-sensitive paper is available through science supply houses; it is also stocked by some toy stores.

Before beginning the experiment, ask any students who have known allergies to sunscreens to avoid contact with them.

The acrylic sheet allows all solar radiation to pass through. Any sunlight passing through the sunscreen will therefore reach the sun-sensitive paper.

ANALYSIS

7. a. Describe your results.

Higher SPF ratings offer the most sun protection.

_____

b. Which lotion offered the most protection? __highest SPF__ the least? __0 SPF__

c. Is there a noticeable difference in protection from one SPF rating to the next?

There may be little noticeable difference in protection between similar SPF grades.

There should be a pronounced difference between low-SPF and high-SPF lotions.

8. Which lotion would you recommend to someone who anticipates being in the sun for a long period of time? Why?

For extended exposure to the sun, the higher the SPF factor, the better. The longer the

exposure to the sun, the more damage done to the skin by UV rays. High-SPF lotions

filter out more of the harmful rays, reducing total UV exposure. With a high-SPF lotion,

total UV exposure remains low even after extended exposure to the sun.

9. What variables could have affected your results?

Variables include the age of the lotion, the brand of lotion, the intensity of sunlight

(which depends on latitude, time of day, season, altitude, and amount of cloudiness);

the thickness of the layer of lotion applied, the relative transparency of the acrylic

sheets to UV rays, the sensitivity of the paper, and the length of exposure to sunlight.

10. Which lotion was the control in this experiment?

The non-SPF lotion (with no suncreen) was the control.

11. How might you change this experiment to better control your variables?

Use the same brand of lotion for every SPF grade; use only recently manufactured

lotion; find a way to apply a uniform layer of each grade of lotion to the paper.

_____

GOING FURTHER

12. Collect sunglasses and test their degree of UV protection by placing the lenses on sheets of sun-sensitive paper and conducting the experiment again.

Extension:
Have students test different brands of sunscreen with the same SPF rating.

Name_____ Class _____ Date _____

8.1

CHANGING LANDSCAPES

How has the landscape of your area changed over time? The landscape of the United States has changed dramatically as land use has changed. *Land use* refers to how humans use land, such as for farming, industry, recreation, or housing.

One aspect of the landscape that changes through land use is *land cover*—the natural plant communities, such as forest and grassland, that exist in a given area. The number of people per unit land area is called *population density*. Land cover is usually capable of absorbing the effects of low-density human populations. The population of the continental United States has greatly increased in the last few decades, while the land area has stayed the same.

In this Investigation, you will determine the extent of local landscape changes by studying aerial photographs and maps of your area. As part of a land-use planning group, you will create a land use map to evaluate changes in the landscape. Keep your pencils sharp—and your eyes sharper.

EXAMINE THE LAY OF THE LAND

1. Your teacher will provide you with a United States Geological Survey (USGS) quadrangle map that includes the study area. Examine the map closely. What types of land use in the study area are apparent from the map?

   <u>Answers will vary. Possible types of land uses that students may observe include</u>

   <u>forested land, cropland, and urban land</u>

   _____

   _____

2. Look carefully at the two aerial photos of this area. One is a recent shot, and the other is an older aerial photo of the area. These photos may be at different scales, so features may look larger or smaller. Are there any other obvious differences between the photos? What changes in the landscape do you notice?

   <u>Answers will vary.</u> _____

   _____

   _____

   _____

MATERIALS

- highlighter pen
- metric ruler
- calculator
- magnifying lens
- transparency grids
- colored pencils
- USGS quadrangle map*
- 2 aerial photos*

Groups of 4–6 students work well for this activity.

*United States Geological Survey (USGS) quadrang!e maps are available through the USGS as well as at most map retailers.

*You may order the aerial photos on-line at the USGS Global Land Information System Web site or by calling 1-800-USA-MAPS. Order the photos by faxing the portion of the quadrangle map that includes the study area to any USGS Earth Science Information Center. Request the recent photo (taken in the 1990s) and another photo at least 20 years older. The scale may vary, but USGS will ensure that both photos include the study area. The maps and photos may take 2–5 weeks to arrive when ordered from USGS.

If possible, choose several study areas. When you select the study area(s), make sure there are a variety of land uses. Try to select an area that includes the edge of your city or town because city edges tend to contain a variety of land uses. Copies of the maps and photos may be used if several groups have the same study area.

INVESTIGATION 8.1, CONTINUED

Remind students that urban areas have a population density of at least 5,000 people per square mile. Since students cannot measure population from aerial photos, tell them to gauge the level of urbanization by visually gauging how compact the human development is.

Have the students determine whether the study area is primarily urban, suburban, or rural.

3. Locate any populated areas in the older photograph. Use a magnifying lens to pick out buildings. Buildings cast a shadow, so look for a white/black pattern. Are the buildings placed close together, or are they spread out over the study area? Is the current populated area urban? If not, what is it?

Answers will vary. If the photos provide enough resolution, students should draw a

distinction between urban and suburban land use.

_____

_____

4. Notice whether there are any dark areas in the older photo. Dark areas are usually wooded areas, such as pine forests. Compare any forest cover in the older photo with that in the recent photo. How has the forest cover changed?

Answers will vary._____

_____

_____

_____

5. Find evidence of non-forested plant cover in the older photo. Cropland usually appears as uniform rectangles or circles, while rangeland and grassland appears with more texture and less-precise borders. How has the non-forested plant cover changed in the recent photo? What do you think might account for these changes?

Answers will vary._____

_____

_____

_____

6. Look for barren areas—places where soil and rock are exposed—in the original photo. Is there evidence of erosion? Are there any new barren areas in the recent photo? If so, do you think these changes are the result of human activity or natural processes?

Answers will vary._____

_____

_____

_____

MAP THE STUDY AREA

7. Place a transparency grid over the original photo, and trace the study area on the transparency. Trace the borders of the areas of different land use, and fill in each area with a different color. You have just created a land use map! Do the same for the recent photo.

8. Count the graph squares within each land-use border on your map, and write the number in the table below. Calculate the percentage of the total land area devoted to each land-use type, and write this data in the "Original photo" column in the chart below. Repeat this step for the recent photo.

Study Area Data Collection Table

Original photo			Recent photo		
Land-use type	Number of squares	Percent	**Land-use type**	Number of squares	Percent
Urban/suburban			Urban/suburban		
Cropland			Cropland		
Rangeland/grassland			Rangeland/grassland		
Forested land			Forested land		
Water bodies			Water bodies		
Wetland			Wetland		
Exposed soil and rock			Exposed soil and rock		
Total		100%	Total		100%

9. Use the data above to complete the pie charts below.

Original Land-Use

Answers will vary.

Recent Land-Use

Answers will vary.

Natural land cover may gradually take over areas that were previously farmed or harvested for timber.

ANALYZE THE CHANGING LANDSCAPE

10. Has the overall land cover changed since the original photo was taken? Explain what might account for these changes.

Answers will vary.

_____

_____

_____

Suburban land use is similar to urban land use in that both substitute paved areas and infrastructure for natural land cover. However, suburban sprawl is characterized by low population densities, so a given number of people tend to use a relatively large area of land. Urban land use spreads out over a smaller area, but uses more natural resources to support the dense populations that live there.

Geographers and planners also try to forecast trends in order to plan for future urban and suburban growth.

11. Has the total area devoted to urban and suburban land use increased since the original photo was taken? If so, what other type(s) of land use and land cover have diminished?

Answers will vary.

_____

_____

_____

12. Given what you have learned about land use trends in the study area, how do you think the land will change in the next 20 years? Explain your answer.

Answers will vary. Students should base their prediction on the trends illustrated by

comparing the two aerial photos.

_____

_____

As an extension, go to the USGS Web site and look up Earthshots, which links satellite images to articles regarding environmental change.

13. Think about how the anticipated changes in land use will affect the land cover of the study area. As a member of a local planning group, what recommendations would you make regarding future land use in the study area?

Answers will vary. Students should try to balance the need for urban growth

with the need to preserve the land and natural resources on which human

populations depend.

_____

INVESTIGATION 9.1

MANAGING THE MOISTURE IN GARDEN SOIL

You work as a soil specialist with the Bucolic County Soil Conservation District. One day, you receive the following letter from a local resident.

LN

Dear Sir or Madam,

My family recently started a small organic vegetable garden in our backyard in hopes of growing cheaper, fresher, and more healthful food than we can buy at the store. Unfortunately, we find that we must water our garden very often to keep it healthy, and our water bills are skyrocketing. What can we do to reduce the amount of water our garden needs? If the high water bills continue, we may have to give up this "money-saving" project.

Sincerely,

Latisha Norton

Mrs. Latisha Norton

MATERIALS

- soil sample
- metric balance
- crucible (or other heat-safe container)
- tongs
- heat source (Bunsen burner, hot plate, or oven)
- stirring rod
- funnel
- filter paper
- water
- eyedropper
- 250 mL beaker or cup
- watch (or clock)
- at least three of the following: chopped leaves; chopped sphagnum moss; decayed wood fiber; sawdust; flour; compost; cow manure; chopped grass clippings; Terrasorb® granules; other materials

Groups of 3 to 4 students work well for this activity.

When you read Mrs. Norton's letter, you realize that a likely problem is that water drains out of her garden soil too quickly. In order to give Mrs. Norton advice on how to improve her soil, you want to find out how much water it can hold. After calling to discuss the situation, you visit her garden and collect several soil samples.

You may want to save time by pre-drying the samples and storing them in plastic bags to avoid accumulation of moisture.

It is very important that soil samples are dried but not burned. An incubator set at 100°F works well, as does an oven set on warm (although it may produce an unpleasant odor).

As the soil is very dry, students may need to mix the water with the soil to ensure that the soil is saturated.

1. Dry your soil sample without burning organic matter. To do this, place about 50 g of soil in a crucible or other heat-safe container. Using tongs, gently heat it over a Bunsen burner or hot plate or put it in an oven. Stir the sample occasionally with a stirring rod to ensure complete drying.

2. After the sample is completely dry, weigh out about 10 g of dry soil. Record its exact mass in the table on the next page.

3. Dampen a circle of filter paper until it is thoroughly moist, but not dripping. Weigh the moist filter paper, and record its mass in the table.

4. Fold the filter paper into quarters, and then open it as shown in the illustration to form a "cup" that fits in a funnel. Place the filter paper in the funnel.

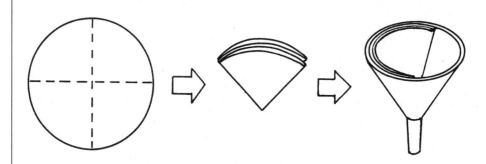

5. Place the dry soil sample on the filter paper in the funnel. Place the funnel in a small beaker or cup.

6. Add water to the soil sample one drop at a time until all of the soil is moist and water begins to drip out of the funnel. Stop adding water, and set the funnel aside for 5 minutes.

INVESTIGATION 9.1, CONTINUED

7. After 5 minutes, remove the filter paper and moist soil from the funnel, and weigh them together. Record their mass in the table.

8. Calculate the mass of the moistened soil sample (**D**) by subtracting the mass of the damp filter paper (**B**) from the mass of the completely moistened sample with filter paper (**C**). Record the result in the table.

9. Calculate the amount of water that your soil sample can hold (**E**) by subtracting the mass of the dry soil sample (**A**) from the mass of the moistened soil sample (**D**). Record the result in the table.

10. Calculate the percent water-holding capacity of your sample (**F**) by dividing the mass of water held (**E**) by the mass of the moistened soil sample (**D**) and multiplying by 100. The higher the percent water-holding capacity, the more water the soil can hold. Record the result in the table.

	A Mass of dry soil	B Mass of damp filter paper	C Mass of moistened sample with filter paper	D Mass of moistened sample (C–B)	E Mass of water held (D–A)	F Percent water- holding capacity (E/D)×100
Unmodified sample						
Sample mixed with: _____						
Sample mixed with: _____						
Sample mixed with: _____						

11. Compare your results with those of your classmates, or perform the same test on different samples. Which soil sample had the best water-holding capacity? Why do you think this is so?

Answers will vary depending on soil samples tested. Sandy soils will hold less water

than clay soils because sand particles and the pores (spaces) between them are much

larger than the particles and pores in clay, allowing water to drain out more readily.

12. Divide the remaining dry soil sample into three 5 g portions. To each portion, add 5 g of any one of the following materials: chopped dry leaves; chopped dry sphagnum moss; dry decayed wood fiber; sawdust; flour; dry compost; dry cow manure; dry chopped grass clippings; Terrasorb® granules; or other materials that you bring or are provided by your teacher. Make sure that any material you use is thoroughly dry before blending it with the soil. Weigh each mixed soil sample, and record the masses in the table on the previous page.

13. Perform steps 3 through 10 for your mixed soil samples. Record your results in the table.

14. Which additive improved the soil's water-holding capacity the most? Why do you think this is so?

Answers will vary depending on materials used. Terrasorb® will give best results if

available. In general, materials made up of small particles will hold more water than

materials with larger particles, due to the greater surface area of the particles.

_____

_____

15. Based on your experimental results as well as your reading on this subject, what could you recommend to Mrs. Norton to reduce the amount of water her garden needs?

Add Terrasorb® or organic matter in the form of manure or compost. Keep the soil

covered at all times with a mulch or cover crop to reduce evaporation.

_____

_____

I N V E S T I G A T I O N

9.2

MODELING PESTICIDE POLLUTION

Congratulations! You've just been hired by the Fluterton County Water Safety Service as director of field research. Your first assignment is to respond to the following letter from a concerned resident of the county.

Director of Field Research
Fluterton County
Water Safety Service
P.O. Box 3001
Fluterton, IL 61807

Dear Sir or Madam:

We recently had our well water tested for the first time in a few years. When the results came back, they showed contaminants that were not there before: trace amounts of a pesticide that was used many years ago on some nearby farms, as well as small amounts of several petroleum products. First of all, how could a pesticide that was used 20 years ago suddenly affect our water today? Also, we've noticed that the litter problem around here has been getting pretty bad lately. Is that going to contaminate our water too? If so, when? As you might imagine, we are more than a little concerned.

Sincerely,

Tracey Watson

Tracey Watson

MATERIALS

- bottom two-thirds of a clear, 2 L soda bottle
- light-colored sand
- light-colored aquarium gravel
- piece of nylon stocking
- small rubber band
- spray nozzle and tube from a spray bottle
- red food coloring
- blue watercolor paint in solid form
- 500 mL beaker
- paper cup
- water

Groups of 2 to 3 students work well for this activity.

In the course of your research, you find the following passage in a water safety journal:

> In the United States, about one-fifth of our fresh water comes from underground sources. Homes that rely on wells are just one example of groundwater use. Wells are drilled down to where the ground is saturated, and the water stored there is pumped up to the surface. Aquifers and other groundwater sources are replenished gradually by surface water that seeps down through the soil; unfortunately, this water can often contain particulates, dissolved chemicals, and other substances that contaminate the groundwater.

Building a model of a well will allow you to address Ms. Watson's concerns. With your model, you will not only investigate the process by which groundwater sources become polluted, but also see how different types of pollution from the surface can eventually end up in well water.

BUILD A WELL

1. Fill the soda bottle about half full with aquarium gravel.

2. Fold the piece of nylon stocking several times, and place it across the open end of the sprayer tube. Secure it tightly with the rubber band. Insert the tube into the gravel along the side of the bottle—the end of the tube should be about 3 cm from the bottom.

3. Add water until it just covers the gravel. Then add sand to about 3 cm from the top of the bottle. Pump the nozzle a few times to get the flow of water started. Spray the water into the beaker.

An important part of this lab is keeping the tube and nozzle from becoming clogged with sand. To help prevent this, make sure the nylon stocking is attached securely to the tube; tape may be necessary in some cases. Also, wetting the sand slightly before adding it to the soda bottle will help keep the sand from falling immediately through the gravel to the bottom.

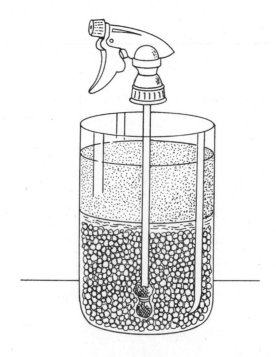

4. Pump the nozzle and observe the water level in the soda bottle. What happens?

The water level goes down as the nozzle is pumped.

5. With your pencil, punch a few small holes in the bottom of the paper cup. To simulate precipitation, fill the cup with water and let the water drizzle out through the holes onto the sand. Try to avoid stirring up the sand, because this may cause the sand to seep down and clog the tube. Practice adding precipitation while you pump the well until you can add and remove water at about the same rate.

ADD SOME POLLUTION

6. Place 10 drops of red food coloring on top of the sand. This represents pollution, such as pesticides or other chemicals, that is dissolved in surface runoff. Begin pumping the well and adding precipitation. As you proceed, be sure that the water level stays between the surface of the sand and the end of the tube. Watch for red coloration to appear in your discharge beaker. How many squeezes of the trigger does it take for the food coloring to pass through the well?

Answers will vary.

7. Is your well polluted permanently? Explain.

No; eventually, all of the food coloring would be pumped out of the water source.

This would take a long time, however.

8. Place a few crumbled bits of blue paint on top of the sand. This represents waste or other solid pollutants that contaminate groundwater by dissolving in surface water that seeps into the ground. Repeat the process described in step 6. How many squeezes does it take for the color to appear this time?

Answers will vary.

9. Explain why the food coloring passed through the well at a different rate than did the crumbled paint.

In general, the paint passes through the well more slowly because it has to dissolve

before it can contaminate the water to a noticeable degree.

10. Explain how a different rate of precipitation would affect the speed at which a pollutant shows up in the pumped water.

    More precipitation would cause the pollutant to sink into the ground (and thus pollute

    the water) faster.

RESPOND TO THE PUBLIC'S CONCERNS

Extension:
Have students contact the local or state Environmental Protection Agency (EPA) office to find out what substances are considered pollutants in drinking water. This agency can also provide information on the levels of these substances that are considered safe.

11. In Ms. Watson's letter, she asked: "How could a pesticide used 20 years ago suddenly affect our water today?" Using what you've learned about ground-water pollution, how would you answer this question?

    The pollutant takes a long time to soak down into the soil and pollute the ground-

    water source.

12. She also asked if the growing litter problem in the area could affect her water supply. Do you think this is a valid concern? Explain.

    Any water-soluble substances in the litter will eventually dissolve and be carried

    underground by precipitation soaking into the ground. These substances may then

    show up in the water supply.

Point out the potential range of pollutants, many of which are colorless. Challenge the students to think of ways to detect these "invisible" compounds.

13. From the rates at which a liquid (the food coloring) and a solid (the paint) passed through your well, you can establish a ratio of the liquid rate to the solid rate. Assuming for the moment that this ratio applies to all types of liquids and solids, calculate how long it will take for the litter problem to affect Ms. Watson's water supply.

    Sample answer: If the food coloring took 40 squeezes to appear in the discharge

    beaker and the paint took 50 squeezes, then 20 years × 5/4 = 25 years for the litter

    contaminants to affect the water supply. Point out to students that this comparison is

    oversimplified and serves only to demonstrate a trend.

INVESTIGATION 9.3

WHICH CROPS TOLERATE SALT?

County of Dixon
Road Services Extension Office

Dear extension officers:
Every year, we have significant snowfall and ice on our roads. I appreciate your efforts to make the roads safe for travel, but every spring I become concerned about the damage done by this road clearing. In particular, I am worried that the salt used to melt snow and ice harms the crops we have planted near Route 4. I wonder if you could tell me which kinds of crop plants can best tolerate the yearly accumulation of salt. Thanks for your help.

Yours truly,

Joan Smith

When Joan Smith's letter arrives at the county office, Extension Officer Tom Watts is curious. He's not aware of any especially salt-tolerant crops, so he decides to use this question as the basis for an investigation. He decides the best way to find plants that tolerate salt is to raise seeds from different plants using different concentrations of saltwater solutions and find out which seeds survive best.

MATERIALS

- table salt
- 1 gal. sealable plastic bags (4)
- measuring cup and spoon
- 3 L plastic bottles with caps (4)
- funnel
- paper towels
- stapler
- permanent marking pen
- plant seeds: alfalfa, clover, wild rye, wheat grass, and fescue
- small pots and soil (optional)

Crop-plant seeds are very inexpensive and can be obtained from farm supply stores or well-stocked nurseries.

The more dilutions students use, the more precise their results will be.

PROCEDURE

1. How could Tom state the problem he's investigating?

   Which crop plants best tolerate salt?

2. First, make a very concentrated saltwater solution by mixing 300 g of table salt in 3 L of water. Store this solution in a sealed 3 L bottle for 24 hours. This is the "0% dilution"; it's not diluted at all.

3. Choose and prepare three dilutions of this standard solution. Use the table below to find out how much of the standard solution to mix with a given amount of fresh water for each dilution. For example, to make a 60 percent dilution, mix 200 mL of the standard solution with 300 mL of fresh water. Make sure to label each solution bottle.

Dilution Recipes		
Dilution	**Standard solution (control)**	**Fresh water**
0% (control)	500 mL	0 mL
10%	450 mL	50 mL
20%	400 mL	100 mL
30%	350 mL	150 mL
40%	300 mL	200 mL
50%	250 mL	250 mL
60%	200 mL	300 mL
70%	150 mL	350 mL
80%	100 mL	400 mL
90%	50 mL	450 mL
100%	0 mL	500 mL

INVESTIGATION 9.3, CONTINUED

4. List the dilutions you made below.

<u>Answers will vary.</u>_____

5. Use the plastic sealable bags as germination chambers. You will need one bag for each salt dilution you plan to test. Cut or fold a paper towel and fit 2 to 4 layers flat inside each plastic bag.

Using plastic sealable bags and paper towels is an easy, effective, and inexpensive way to germinate many kinds of seeds.

6. Starting at the bottom of the bag, make a row of 10 evenly spaced seeds using one kind of seed. Use the marking pen to label this row on the plastic bag. Separate this row of seeds from the next row by stapling several staples across the width of the bag. The seeds should be visible through one side of the bag.

Help students make sure that each bag contains the same seed selection.

7. Repeat step 5 for the remaining flour seed types. Why is it important to put each seed type in a separate row?

<u>so the type can be identified and associated with its response to a specific salt</u>

<u>dilution</u>_____

8. Lightly moisten the entire paper towel with 15 mL of one dilution of saltwater and seal the bag. With the marking pen, label the bag with its saltwater dilution.

9. Repeat steps 5–8 for each saltwater dilution. Make sure that you use fresh water (100% dilution) for one bag of seeds. Why is it important to use fresh water in one bag of seeds?

<u>This bag is the control. It demonstrates that seeds will germinate without salt.</u>

_____

10. Set aside each of the prepared dilutions. Place the bags out of direct sunlight and away from heat for 10 days. Water them daily with the same saltwater dilution initially used. After 10 days, record your observations in the data chart below.

Tell students that monocotyledons, also known as monocots, are plants characterized by embryos containing only one leaf. Dicotyldeons (dicots) are plants whose embryos contain two leaves. Generally, monocots are more tolerant to salt than dicots. Grasses, such as wheat and rye, are examples of monocots. Alfalfa and clover are examples of dicots.

		Germination Success	
Seed type	Number of seeds planted	Number of seeds germinated	Percent germination (number germinated/ number planted)

11. Based on your results, what seeds can Tom Watts recommend for planting in salty areas?

Results will vary. Monocot grasses, such as wheat and wild rye, should be more

successful in salt than dicot plants, such as alfalfa and clover.

_____

12. Alfalfa and clover develop a single main root, called a taproot, while fescue, wheat grass, and wild rye have branching root systems. Based on your results, is there a correlation between root type and salt tolerance?

Answers will vary. Wheat grass and wild rye should be better able to survive the

saltier dilutions, indicating that the fanlike root systems of grasses increase their salt

tolerance.

_____

13. Use the second data table below to summarize your class results.

Class Results for Germination Success				
Dilution (control)	Germination success by seed type			
0%				
10%				
20%				
30%				
40%				
50%				
60%				
70%				
80%				
90%				
100%				

14. Why is it important to know what percentage of the control group (100% dilution) germinated?

Sometimes seeds don't germinate, even under ideal conditions, and so it's important to establish a baseline germination rate to use to compare other germination percentages. For example, if 90% of the seeds germinate with both fresh water and salt water, we could conclude that salt has no effect. On the other hand, if the percentage of germination in the control group is significantly greater, we can conclude that seeds are harmed by salt.

15. What percentage of the control group germinated?

Answers will vary. Good germination results are between 75 and 85 percent.

16. Which seeds are the most salt-tolerant? How can you tell?

Answers will vary depending on the plant varieties tested. The seeds that have the highest percent germination rate in the highest concentration of salt solution are the most salt-tolerant.

EXTENSION

Here is a method for doing a more comprehensive test of plants' salt tolerance. Start with the germinated seeds used in the Investigation. Transfer each row of seeds to a separate pot filled with peat, which is composed of decaying plant matter. Label each pot with the seed type and the dilution of the standard saltwater solution. Water all of the seeds with tap water that was left at room temperature overnight. Maintain the same light and temperature levels for all plants during the course of the experiment. Continue watering the seeds every other day with 15 mL of "aged" tap water. After 8 weeks, water the plants every other day with 5–10 mL of the same dilution that you indicated on the pots. Evaluate the effect of salt concentration by comparing the percentage of plants that survive at different concentrations.

INVESTIGATION 10.1

DIVERSITY IN A DROP

Within any ecosystem, organisms form a complex web of physical, chemical, and biological interactions. The health of an ecosystem depends on the involvement of all of the organisms, whether they are producers, consumers, or decomposers. When any part of the web is disrupted or destroyed, the whole ecosystem suffers.

   In this Investigation, you will study biodiversity in an aquatic environment. By altering the physical characteristics of your ecosystem, you will be able to see how biodiversity can be affected. From your results, you will infer the effects of physical changes on biodiversity in natural ecosystems.

INITIAL OBSERVATIONS

1. Obtain a sample of pond water. Swirl the water gently. Then use the eyedropper to place a drop or two on a microscope slide. Cover the drops with a coverslip. If you have too much water, use the corner of a paper towel to absorb the excess water.

2. Set the microscope to medium power, and examine your slide. (If you are unable to see organisms at first, try looking at other parts of the slide or preparing a new slide.) Locate bright green organisms; these are algae (producers). The green color comes from chlorophyll, a pigment that allows photosynthesis to occur. Also look for moving organisms; these are protozoa (unicellular consumers). They may be clear, brown, or slightly green (from having consumed algae). Then switch your microscope to its highest power. At the edge of a clump of algae, look for tiny wriggling forms; these are bacteria (decomposers in most cases). Using the space below, sketch and label all of the organisms that are visible on your microscope slide.

3. How is the role of the producers (the algae) in this ecosystem different from the role of the decomposers (the bacteria)?

   Producers use light energy and nutrients to manufacture their own food, while the

   decomposers feed on decaying organic matter and return nutrients to the water.

   _____

   _____

   _____

   _____

MATERIALS

- microscope
- microscope slides with coverslips
- eyedropper
- pH paper
- pond water containing mud and algae
- 1 L clear container with a lid
- one of the following: 10 mL bleach, 10 mL vinegar, or 1 g fertilizer
- funnel
- paper towel
- stirring rod

Groups of 2 to 4 students work well for this activity.

Use empty jars or soda bottles for the containers.

Collect a sample of 4 or 5 L of water from a local, natural, open watershed. Make sure that the sample includes some algae and a small amount of mud. Preview the sample to be sure that all desired organisms can be identified.

When collecting pond water, a plankton net is helpful for concentrating microorganisms in the sample.

ALTERING THE ECOSYSTEM

4. Test the pH of the sample. State the pH and indicate whether it is acidic, neutral, or basic.

   The sample will probably be close to neutral (pH = 7), but it may be slightly acidic

   (pH < 7) or basic (pH > 7).

You may wish to prepare these containers the appropriate number of days ahead of time so that students can complete this Investigation during one class period.

5. Carefully read each of the following procedures for altering the ecosystem, and pick one to carry out.

   Procedure A: Transfer approximately 400 mL of your sample to a sealed container. Be sure to include algae and a small amount of mud. Place the container in a cool, dark location for 3 to 5 days.

   Procedure B: Transfer approximately 800 mL of your sample to an open, clear container. Add 1 g of houseplant fertilizer to the sample, and swirl the water gently to dissolve the fertilizer. Place the container in a location that receives direct sunlight for 3 to 5 days.

   Procedure C: Transfer approximately 600 mL of your sample to an open, clear container. Add 10 mL of household bleach (a base), and place the container in a location that receives indirect sunlight for 1 to 2 days.

   Procedure D: Transfer approximately 600 mL of your sample to an open, clear container. Add 10 mL of household vinegar (an acid), and place the container in a location that receives indirect sunlight for 1 to 2 days.

   Which procedure did you choose? **Each student group should choose one procedure.**

6. Each of the above procedures involves a physical and/or chemical change to the ecosystem. What do you predict will happen to the biodiversity of your ecosystem when you carry out your chosen procedure?

   Accept all reasonable responses.

   _____

   _____

7. Carry out the procedure you have chosen. Be sure to label your container with your names and the letter of procedure.

ANALYZING THE RESULTS

8. After the appropriate number of days have passed, prepare a microscope slide of the sample as you did earlier. Examine the slide under the microscope. Test the pH of the water in the sample. Compare your findings with your initial observations. What differences do you observe?

Answers may vary. In general, however, the following will be observed. Procedure A:

The algae will be darker, and many will be dead; protozoa may move more slowly or

be dead; bacteria will be abundant; the pH will be similar to its initial value.

Procedure B: There will be an abundance of bright green algae; other organisms will

be scarce; the pH will be more basic (higher than its initial value). Procedure C:

Relatively more algae will be present; the pH will be more basic (higher). Procedure D:

Relatively more bacteria will be present; the pH will be more acidic (lower).

9. How has the biodiversity of organisms in the ecosystem changed?

If all of the original organisms are observed, the biodiversity is unchanged. However,

in most cases, not all of the organisms can be observed, in which case biodiversity

has declined.

10. Did the different types of organisms in the ecosystem show different degrees of sensitivity to the changes in their environment? Explain.

The organisms that declined most in number can be considered the most sensitive to

the changes. In some cases (such as the algae exposed to fertilizer), certain organ-

isms will thrive in response to the changes.

_____

11. Discuss your results with students who followed different procedures. Which of the four procedures do you think was the most destructive to the ecosystem? Explain your answer.

Answers will vary; students should offer reasonable explanations for their choices.

_____

_____

_____

_____

INVESTIGATION 10.1, CONTINUED

12. So far, only short-term effects of changes to the physical and chemical characteristics of an environment have been discussed. Imagine that a change similar to **Procedure B** (artificial eutrophication) occurred in a pond in a wilderness area. What would be the long-term effects of this change?

Algae would multiply rapidly, forming algae blooms and overpopulating the pond. As

the algae began to die and decompose, large amounts of the pond water's dissolved

oxygen would be used up, causing fish and other organisms to suffocate in the

oxygen-depleted water.

_____

_____

13. Why must the management of an ecosystem take into account the need for biological diversity?

Each of the organisms that take part in an ecosystem's web of interactions is neces-

sary to maintain the health of the ecosystem.

_____

_____

_____

_____

_____

_____

INVESTIGATION 10.2

DESIGNING A PRESERVE

MATERIALS
- tracing paper
- colored pencils
- metric ruler
- topographic map
- field guides of local animals and plants

A United States Geological Survey topographic map works well for this lab. You can also use a TOPO interactive map, available on CD-ROM, and print out the map area you wish to work with.

This activity works well with teams of 2 to 4 students.

The organisms alive today are the products of millions of years of evolutionary history and can never be replaced if they are lost. Yet much of the Earth's biodiversity is seriously threatened. Scientists estimate that nearly 20 percent of all species will become extinct in the next half century if current trends continue. Concerned people are trying to devise ways to save as many species as possible. Zoos, seed banks, botanical gardens, and arboreta are part of the solution. However, most species cannot be sustained for long outside their native ecosystems. For this reason, scientists believe it is crucial to set aside protected areas, or *nature preserves,* where species can live undisturbed by human development.

A successful preserve requires careful planning. Size and shape are the most important considerations. A preserve should be large enough to sustain a healthy population of many different species, including those at the top of food chains. It should also encompass a variety of ecosystem types—such as grassland, forest, and wetland—so that it protects a broad range of species. However, if it is possible to preserve only a relatively small area, it may be more important to protect as much of the rarest ecosystem as possible. Preserve designers must balance all of these considerations. In this Investigation, you will design a preserve "in your own backyard"—that is, in the area surrounding your hometown.

EVALUATE YOUR ECOSYSTEM

1. Brainstorm about one or more ecosystems in your area that are threatened by human development.

   Answers will vary but may include wetlands such as streams and mashes.

2. On tracing paper, use your ruler to create a 16 cm × 20 cm rectangle for a total area of 320 cm². This will be the size of the area you can consider in deciding where to locate your preserve. Divide this rectangle into 20 subdivisions, or *quadrates.* Each quadrate should be 4 cm × 4 cm (16 cm²).

3. Examine the topographic map. Place your tracing paper over a natural area that is next to at least one town, and that includes several kinds of ecosystems. Trace the topographic contour lines with black pencil, and the streams and lakes with blue pencil. Lightly shade different ecosystem types with different colors, and trace roads and other human-built infrastructures. Be consistent with your symbols and colors so that similar features are coded the same way.

4. Think about the plants and animals that are likely to live in the area you have traced. Consult field guides for information on the habitat requirements of different species. Next, refer to the energy pyramid on page 61 of the textbook, and select two or more representative species for each of four trophic levels. These species will represent the local biodiversity.

5. Look again at the topographic map. It should have a map key along the bottom. Create a key on your tracing paper in the bottom left-hand corner. Include the scale the map is drawn to as well as labeled symbols for the features you have included. Next include the organisms you chose in step 4. Write the common species name followed by the scientific name. Then draw a symbol representing that organism to the right of its scientific name. For example, a small red maple leaf could represent maple trees and a black mask could represent raccoons.

6. Determine how many individuals of each species would probably live in the area you have chosen. In your field guide, look up the habitat requirements, or range, of the top carnivores you have chosen. Then use the 10× rule expressed in the energy pyramid to determine reasonable numbers for species on lower trophic levels. To the right of each organism's symbol, write the number of individuals represented by that symbol. For instance, one maple leaf could represent 25 maple trees.

Species in My Area			
Plant species name	Estimated number	Animal species name	Estimated number

7. Draw your species symbols in places where the species are most likely to occur. Again, remember that the total number of individual plants should be about 10 times larger that the total number of primary consumers, and so on, up the food chain.

PLAN YOUR PRESERVE

8. Imagine that your town government and a local developer are going to build homes, shopping malls, roads, and other infrastructure on 80 percent of your traced area. They will set aside 20 percent of the area as a nature preserve. They have hired you to plan the size and shape of this preserve. Calculate how large an area you can preserve in terms of quadrates, and write your answer below.

0.2 × 20 quadrates = 4 quadrates' worth of area

9. You decide to preserve as much biodiversity as possible. But how does one measure biodiversity? Scientists use several indicators to estimate the diversity of species living in an area. One indicator is *species richness,* the number of species present in a given area. Determine the species richness of each quadrate by counting the number of species present. For example, if there are five species in a given quadrate, then the species richness is 5. Another indicator of biodiversity is the number of trophic levels present, or the *trophic level richness.* Refer to pages 60 and 61 of your textbook to review the concept of trophic levels. Determine the trophic level richness by determining how many trophic levels there are among the species in your community. For example, if a quadrate contains plants, crickets, and toads, then the quadrate contains 3 trophic levels. Tally the organisms present in each quadrate, and record the species richness and trophic level richness in the chart below.

Indicators of Species Diversity										
Quadrate	1	2	3	4	5	6	7	8	9	10
Species richness										
Trophic level richness										
Quadrate	11	12	13	14	15	16	17	18	19	20
Species richness										
Trophic level richness										

10. Which quadrate has:

the most species richness? **Answers will vary.** _____

the most trophic level richness? **Answers will vary.** _____

11. Although your preserve must be four quadrates in size, its boundaries do not have to correspond to quadrate boundaries. In other words, your preserve can be whatever shape you want. Explain where you intend to locate your preserve, and justify your decision.

   Answers will vary. Students should try to preserve the area with the greatest species

   richness and trophic level richness. It should also encompass several different

   ecosystems.

12. Draw the boundary of your preserve on your map.

13. Does your preserve protect all of the species that you chose in step 4?

   Answers will vary.

14. Why do some areas contain more species than other areas? Think about what determines where species live.

   Answers will vary. In general, areas with the greatest number of habitats will have

   the greatest number of species. Each habitat has a variety of unique niches that in

   turn support species unique to that habitat. So in general, the more habitats present,

   the more species present.

15. The diversity of species living in an area, called *species-level diversity,* is the most commonly used measure of biodiversity, but it is by no means the only one. Scientists also refer to *habitat-level diversity* and *population-level diversity,* among others. What do you think scientists mean by habitat-level diversity? Why might scientists look at biodiversity from perspectives other than at the species level? Provide at least one example to support your viewpoint.

   Habitat-level diversity refers to the variety of habitats present in a given area.

   Scientists might look at biodiversity from other perspectives because species consti-

   tute only one level of ecological organization. For example, considering population-

   level diversity enables scientists to distinguish between areas with the same number

   of species but different numbers of populations of those species.

I N V E S T I G A T I O N 11.1

WHICH IS THE BEST INSULATOR?

When winter temperatures plummet, how do you stay warm? You put on a sweater or a coat, or maybe both. The colder it gets, the more layers you wear. But do you know how these layers keep you warm?

Each layer traps small pockets of air. Air transfers heat very slowly. The transfer of heat from one material to another is called **conduction.** Materials that transfer heat rapidly are called conductors, and those that transfer heat slowly are called insulators. Air, therefore, is a very poor conductor of heat, making it a good insulator. One disadvantage to insulating with air is that air molecules tend to flow in currents, increasing the rate of heat transfer from the air to other materials.

Now you can understand why you wear many layers of clothing when it's cold—so you are enveloped in an insulator that keeps the heat close to your body.

In this activity, you and your partners will test the insulating qualities of various materials. First you will build a device for testing these materials and then you will evaluate the materials' effectiveness using your device.

TEST THE INSULATORS

1. Assemble an insulation tester like the one shown at right. Punch a hole for the thermometer through the center of the plastic lid with the nail.

2. Choose an insulating material to test and use it to fill the space between the inner and the outer containers of your insulation tester. On a separate sheet of paper, draw one diagram indicating the movement of heat if the material is a good insulator and another diagram indicating the movement of heat if the material is a poor insulator. Indicate the movement of heat with arrows.

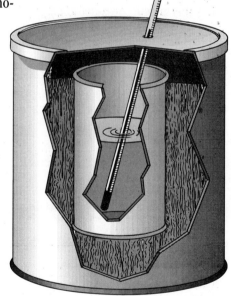

3. Make a table in your notebook to collect temperature data for each insulator. You will note the water temperature every 5 minutes over a 30-minute period.

MATERIALS
- coffee can with lid
- smaller can
- nail
- graduated cylinder
- saucepan or kettle
- heatproof mitt
- outdoor thermometer
- hot plate
- water
- various materials, such as sand, shredded paper, cardboard, sawdust, thick cloth, shredded plastic foam, cotton batting, feathers, wool, vermiculite, rock wool insulation, cellulose insulation, rigid foam insulation, or fiberglass insulation

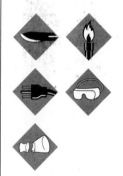

A 2 lb. coffee can works well for the outer container. For the inner container, use a soup can or smaller coffee can. Students should remove paper labels from the cans.

Groups of 3 or 4 students work best for this activity.

Diagrams should show that with a poor insulator, heat is conducted quickly to the outside of the tester. A good insulator traps heat inside the insulation tester.

4. Measure 200 mL of water into a saucepan or kettle. Heat the water on the hot plate until it boils. Wearing the heatproof mitt, pour the water into the inner can. Do not wet the insulation or your results may be affected. **Caution: *Be careful not to spill hot water on yourself or others.***

5. Quickly snap the plastic lid into place, and insert the thermometer so that the bulb is immersed in the water but does not touch the bottom of the inner can. Immediately measure and record the temperature. Continue to take measurements for 30 minutes.

6. Repeat steps 4 and 5 for each insulator you test.

Graphs should vary from a sharp decline for poor insulators to a gradual decline for good insulators.

7. Graph the temperature decline associated with each of the various insulators.

8. Repeat this experiment without using any insulating material. Record the data in a table in your notebook. How effective is air alone as an insulator? If air is a poor conductor of heat, how can you explain your results?

Students should find that air is a poor insulator. Even poor insulating materials

create multiple pockets of air that slow conduction.

9. If time permits, test other materials. Compare your results with those of your classmates. Which material insulated most effectively? least effectively? How was this effectiveness demonstrated?

Answers will vary, but of the materials listed, the most effective insulator is probably

plastic foam; one of the least effective is sand. Effectiveness is demonstrated by a

constant or slowly declining temperature inside the insulation tester.

10. Describe any common characteristics among the most effective insulating materials.

Students should find that the most effective insulators are those that have the most

air pockets. (In some cases, such as with plastic foam insulation, the air pockets may

be hard to see because they are so small.)

11. Do you think that tightly packed insulation would be more effective than loosely packed insulation? Why or why not?

In general, tightly packed insulation is less effective than loosely packed insulation

because tightly packed insulation contains fewer air spaces

INVESTIGATION 11.2

SMOKESTACK IN A BOTTLE

Combustion is a kind of chemical change in which chemical substances are burned to produce energy. Fuels that we burn to warm our homes, generate electricity, or do other useful work are made primarily of carbon, hydrogen, nitrogen, and oxygen. When they *combust,* or burn, these chemicals combine with oxygen and are transformed into new substances. Although some of the products of combustion are invisible to us, their presence in the air contributes to global warming and air pollution. Other combustion products, such as soot, may visibly contribute to the pollution problem. In this laboratory activity, you will use a candle to construct a model of a smokestack in order to study the products of combustion.

GETTING STARTED

1. With a small ball of clay, make a holder for your candle. Insert the candle in the holder and secure it to your work area so that it will not topple over. Then, light the candle.

BLACK SMOKE

2. Imagine that you are the engineer for a "smokestack" energy-producing facility (an energy plant that burns hydrocarbons for fuel). You have noticed that the smoke coming from your stack is blacker than usual. How can you find out where this black material is coming from and what you should do about it? Try some experiments to find out.

   a. Slowly bring the spatula into the orange portion of the candle flame, as shown below.

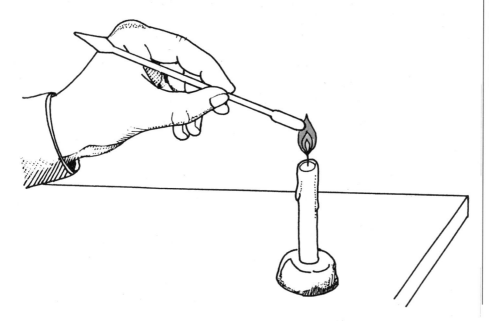

MATERIALS

- 1 gal. glass jar with screw-on lid
- limewater
- candle, 4–6 in. long
- matches
- clay
- metal spatula
- reference books

Groups of 3 to 5 students work well for this activity.

Review with your students that all fossil fuels (petroleum, natural gas, coal) originated from living things composed of atoms of oxygen, hydrogen, carbon, and nitrogen. These atoms cannot be destroyed in chemical processes (conservation of mass) but molecules can be broken apart and recombined to make new compounds.

b. Describe what collects on the metal surface.

Carbon collects on the metal surface because the waxy material of the candle has

not combusted completely in the visible portion of the flame.

c. Where did this material come from? (Hint: What elements do all fuels contain?)

The carbon comes from the incompletely combusted fuel—vaporized wax.

_____

_____

d. Does the flame become "smoky" when you interfere with the incoming air around the flame by placing the spatula in its path?

Yes, the flame becomes smoky.

e. Blow out the candle.

f. Tiny particles suspended in the air are called particulates. They are one form of air pollution that increases the cost of keeping our clothes and furniture clean. More significantly, particulates can also cause health problems. Based on your experiments with the candle flame, what should you do to reduce the particulates given off by your smokestack?

Black smoke arises from the incomplete combustion that occurs due to an inade-

quate supply of oxygen. The power plant must ensure a proper mix of air and fuel in

order for the fuel to burn cleanly.

_____

_____

EMISSIONS TESTING

Part of your job as engineer is to determine what gases are being given off by your smokestack. To do so, you must place your "smokestack" (candle) in a sealed container and test the gases given off with a solution of calcium carbonate (limewater).

3. Secure your unlit candle in the bottom of the jar.

4. Light the candle, and cover the jar with the lid. Allow the candle to burn until it goes out.

Review safety procedures with students and impress on them the seriousness of working with an open flame. Small cartons of baking soda at each work station would provide easily accessible fire extinguishers.

5. Unscrew the lid, and remove the candle as quickly as possible. Pour about a half of an inch of limewater into the bottle. Replace the lid, and shake the contents.

a. What changes do you observe in the limewater?

The limewater becomes cloudy.

b. When limewater is exposed to carbon dioxide, small particles of calcium carbonate become suspended in the liquid, as you have just observed. What was the source of the carbon dioxide?

Carbon dioxide is generated by the combustion process. The carbon originates in

the candle wax, and the oxygen comes from the air.

c. Although carbon dioxide is colorless and odorless, it is not a completely harmless gas in the atmosphere. What is the role of carbon dioxide in the warming of the Earth's atmosphere (global warming)?

It is strongly suspected that carbon dioxide in the atmosphere contributes to global

warming by preventing solar heat from reradiating into space.

HEAVY RAIN

Citizens living near the smokestack facility have been complaining that it rains more in their neighborhood than in other parts of the area. As engineer, you need to find out if any of the gases given off by your smokestack could be partly responsible for this.

6. Dispose of the mixture in the jar as your teacher directs. Carefully dry the inside of the jar, then place the candle back inside.

7. Light the candle, and screw on the lid as before. Carefully observe whether any moisture forms on the inside of the bottle.

a. Do you observe moisture forming in the bottle?

Yes, moisture forms in the bottle.

For disposal, collect mixtures from the entire class in one container. Decant the liquid from the calcium carbonate precipitate and save the solid for future use. Pour the remaining solution down the drain with copious water.

b. Where could this moisture have come from? (Hint: Think about the elements involved in combustion.)

Water, H_2O, is a product of combustion. Hydrogen comes from the fuel, and

oxygen comes from air and, possibly, from the fuel.

c. What will you tell the neighbors about the effect your smokestack has on the climate nearby?

There may be heavier rains due to increased moisture in the local atmosphere.

_____

_____

_____

EXTENSION

A variety of topics could extend from a discussion of the results of this lab, including:

- a more detailed discussion of the chemical processes of combustion, with an emphasis on the similarity between the candle and fossil fuels.

- a discussion of the similarities between the photosynthesis-respiration process in living things and the chemical process of combustion. The disruption of the normal balance of the carbon cycle could be highlighted.

- a discussion of alternative energy sources and of the problems associated with fossil fuels that are avoided through their use.

Another part of your job as engineer is to order new supplies of fuel. You learn about a supplier who can provide fuel at lower cost. However, this fuel is not as pure and contains more nitrogen and sulfur than the fuel you have been using. These elements will react with oxygen in air, giving rise to nitrogen oxides and sulfur oxides. To answer the following questions, you will need to do some research.

8. What effect do nitrogen oxides and sulfur oxides have on the atmosphere and the environment?

Nitrogen oxides and sulfur oxides tend to form nitric and sulfuric acids, which cause

acid rain. Acid rain is harmful to plants and animals, as well as to human construc-

tions such as buildings, statues, and bridges.

_____

_____

_____

9. What factors must you consider in deciding whether or not to use the nitrogen- and sulfur-rich fuels?

Answers will vary, but students should weigh social, health, and environmental

issues against economic factors.

_____

_____

INVESTIGATION 12.1

SANITARY LANDFILLS VS. GARBAGE DUMPS

Garbage dumps used to be major eyesores and ecological nightmares. They smelled terrible, attracted scavengers, such as rats and seagulls, and oozed leachate into water supplies. However, in recent decades engineers have created more environmentally friendly facilities known as *sanitary landfills.* In sanitary landfills, liners prevent liquids from leaking into the soil and contaminating groundwater supplies, and alternating layers of waste and soil all but eliminate odors and scavengers. Some disposal operations even recycle, reuse, and compost organic material. But like most solutions to real-world problems, sanitary landfills have drawbacks, such as increased maintenance costs and space requirements. In this Investigation, you will build a model of a traditional garbage dump and of a modern landfill. You will then compare the two with respect to two important environmental considerations: the rate of decomposition and the amount of pollution produced.

BUILD MODEL LANDFILLS

1. Use the nail to punch holes in the sides and bottom of one bottle. Use the craft knife to carefully cut the tops from both bottles. Save the tops to use in step 3.

2. Place a thin layer of gravel or sand in the bottom of each container. You will need enough mixed garbage to fill each container half-way. In each container, alternate layers of trash and moistened soil to create three layers of each. Add an extra layer of soil on top to control odor and animal pests.

3. Make a few small slits in one of the bottle tops to reduce hazardous gas buildup during the experiment. Carefully tape the top back onto the hole-free bottle. Leave the other bottle open. You now have a model of the each type of landfill.

4. Place each bottle in a shallow pan, and place the setup in an area designated by your teacher.

5. Explain which bottle models a modern sanitary landfill.

   the one without holes and with a top, because the liquid can't leach out

6. Explain which bottle represents a traditional garbage dump.

   the uncovered one with the holes, because the liquid waste leaks out of the "dump"

MATERIALS
- 2 L plastic bottles (2)
- large nail
- 2 craft knives
- soil
- garbage items, such as food, paper, lawn clippings, paper clips, and plastic bags
- fine gravel or sand
- shallow pans
- spray bottle
- heat lamps
- small beaker
- colored pencils
- 12 in. thermometers (2)

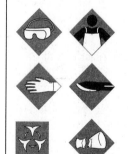

Groups of 2 to 4 students work well in this activity.

BE SURE TO CHECK TRASH BEFOREHAND FOR POTENTIAL HEALTH HAZARDS, SUCH AS SHARP OBJECTS OR CAUSTIC CHEMICALS.

To speed up decomposition, keep the models warm and moist. The bacteria that do most of the decomposing will die if it gets too dry. Place models under a fume hood or outdoors to control odors. If you place the bottles outside, make sure they are safe from disturbance by animals or vandals.

Engineers and urban planners use the same evaluation process when planning a new landfill site.

THINK ABOUT IT

7. What landfill problems concern you most?

Possible concerns include the decay rate of the garbage, the types of gasses produced, the kinds of microbes present, the possibility of groundwater contamination, leachate disposal methods, the attraction of pests and scavengers, and the impact of landfills on solid waste reduction efforts.

8. How might a landfill or its contents adversely affect the environment? How will you determine the environmental impact of each landfill model?

Landfills can potentially pollute the air, water, and soil. Students should realize that the garbage in the perforated bottle could pollute groundwater. An evaluation of each of these threats may be as simple as smelling the landfills, or the students may propose collecting and analyzing gases, runoff, or retained fluid from each landfill model.

OBSERVE CHANGES

For the rest of the experiment you will observe the decay of the materials in the two models and record your observations in the chart on the next page.

Allow several weeks for the garbage to decay noticeably. The experiment may be performed without heat lamps, but decay will be slower. Rate of decay depends on moisture, temperature, soil type, and garbage contents.

Students must wear gloves, protective clothing, and masks when handling the decaying matter.

Tell students that elevated temperatures in their models indicate decay because bacteria generate heat as they break down wastes.

Add the volumes of collected leachate each week to get a cumulative total of leachate. For example, the cumulative total of leachate for 3 weeks is the sum of the amounts of leachate collected from weeks 1, 2, and 3.

9. Switch off the heat lamp 24 hours before making your observations to ensure that the measured temperatures are due only to decomposition. Be careful moving the bottles. Draining leachate may stain clothes and have a foul odor.

10. Rate the changes in the look and smell of each bottle's contents on a scale of 1 to 5, with 1 indicating no change and 5 indicating complete decomposition. For example, if the waste looks unchanged, rate the contents a 1. Record the ratings in the table on the following page. Insert a thermometer through the opening of each bottle into the center of the landfills and wait 5 minutes. Measure and record the temperatures. Be sure to put the cap back on the closed landfill. Measure the volume of the leachate, and record your data in the table. Put the bottles back in the pan.

11. Dampen the soil in the open model with a spray bottle to keep the bacteria active, put the bottles back under the heat lamps, and switch on the lamps.

12. Repeat steps 9–11 once each week for 6 weeks to compare the levels of decay.

	Decay Look (1–5)		Decay Smell (1–5)		Decay Temp. (°C)		Pollution Leachate (in mL)		Brief description	
Decomposition Data										
Week	Open	Closed	Open	Closed	Open	Closed	Open	Closed	Open	Closed
1										
2										
3										
4										
5										
6										

13. After 6 weeks, chart the temperature progression for each model on the middle graph below. Use blue for the open model and red for the closed model. What do you notice about the temperature changes in each model?

The closed model heated more rapidly and stayed hotter than the open model.

Students can record their data on a larger table in their notebooks to allow for more detailed observations.

14. Average the "look" and "smell" ratings for decay, and plot the averages for each week on the left-hand graph below. Use blue and red pencil as you did in step 13. Plot the cumulative volume of leachate per week for each model on the right-hand graph. Is there any relationship between decay and pollution? Write a hypothesis to explain any relationship you find between decay and pollution.

Yes; the rates of both decay and leachate production increase over time.

Hypothesis: The decay of solid waste produces liquid byproducts (leachate),

so the greater the rate of decay, the more leachate that will be produced.

Note: Students can test their hypotheses as an extension to the lab activity.

Indicators of Decomposition

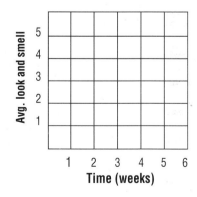
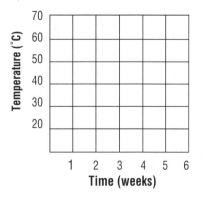
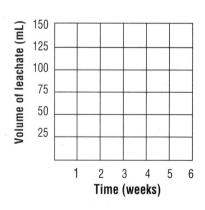

ANALYZE YOUR RESULTS

15. Compare the decay observed in the two types of landfills. What factors do you think encourage or limit decay?

If things progress as planned, students should notice more decay in the traditional landfill. The availability of oxygen and water in this fill encourage decay by both aerobic and anaerobic organisms. In the sanitary fill, exclusion of air and moisture retard decay.

16. Which kinds of garbage items decay most rapidly? most slowly? How might the slow-decaying items pose a long-term environmental threat?

Organic items, such as food and grass clippings, will decay most quickly in both models. Plastic and aluminum items are least prone to decay. The biggest threat from slow-decaying items is that they take up space for long periods of time.

17. How can we reduce the environmental impact of slow-decaying items?

The best way to reduce the impact of slow-decaying items is to reuse and recycle them so that they do not end up in landfills to begin with.

18. Which type of landfill will probably produce less leachate in the short run? in the long run? Explain your answer.

Sanitary landfills produce the least leachate in the short run because they are lined and because decomposition occurs slowly. However, even sanitary landfills eventually leak and pollute. In the long run, because materials decompose more slowly in a sanitary landfill, sanitary landfills will be leaching long after materials from a traditional dump have completely decomposed.

_____

_____

_____

As an extension, students can compare the decomposition in their models to the decomposition in a well-tended compost pile. (You might even have them build their own compost pile.) The comparison would help students understand that decomposition is essential to putting organic elements back into the resource cycle.

INVESTIGATION

12.2

PUTTING ECO-FRIENDLY CLEANSERS TO THE TEST

Supermarket shelves are crammed with products that make our lives easier. Oven cleaners, countertop sprays, toilet-bowl disinfectants, window-cleaning solvents, and countless other household products save us precious time and energy by doing their jobs quickly and with a minimum of effort. Chemicals in the spray-on, wipe-off oven cleaner quickly dissolve the grease and other muck that coats dirty ovens. The bleach you pour in your toilet contains chemicals that kill bacteria and break down chemical stains. But although these products may work well for their intended purposes, their ingredients can be hazardous. If you use these products without strictly following their safety guidelines, you may be endangering your health. And when you throw these products away, you may be releasing hazardous chemicals into the environment.

You might be surprised to discover how many commercial cleansers contain hazardous ingredients. In this investigation, you will survey several commercial products and record information about their hazardous properties. Then, you will make less hazardous, alternative products and test their effectiveness.

BACKGROUND

Cleansers work because a chemical reaction takes place between unwanted matter, mostly dirt and oil, and a cleaning agent. Most cleansers are surface-active chemicals, or *surfactants,* that remove dirt without destroying or damaging the surface to which the dirt is attached. Many cleansers are soaps with additives. Soap cleans because of its molecular properties; one part of a soap molecule is attracted to water while the other is attracted to oil, grease, or fat. The soap molecules surround the oily matter, which can then be rinsed away. Many things can be added to soap to help it work more effectively:

- Mechanical force, such as stirring or scrubbing, helps remove oily dirt.

- An abrasive cleanser combines a powdered abrasive, such as silica or pumice, with soap. An abrasive increases the friction, which removes oil and dirt from the surface more effectively.

Acid-base reactions are also common in household cleansers. For example, metal polishers use a strong acid or base to dissolve rust. Spot and stain removers also rely on the reactivity of strong acids or bases. Other cleaning products work by absorbing unwanted material.

MATERIALS

- soiled household items to be cleaned
- toilet-bowl cleaner
- laundry detergent
- bleach
- oven cleaner
- laundry stain remover
- drain opener
- window cleaner
- furniture polish
- all-purpose cleaner
- ingredients for eco-friendly cleansers: white vinegar, lemon juice, cut lemon, baking soda, washing soda, ammonia, chalk, borax, cream of tartar, olive oil
- mixing bowl
- spoon
- measuring cups
- measuring spoons
- spray bottle
- sponges
- nylon scouring pads
- steel wool
- paper towels
- newspaper

WHAT'S IN THE CUPBOARD?

1. Examine each of the following products: toilet-bowl cleaner, laundry detergent, bleach, oven cleaner, laundry stain remover, drain opener, window cleaner, and furniture polish. **Caution: Some chemicals may leak or there may be harmful residue on the containers.** On a sheet of paper, record the following data about each product:

   - name of product

   - presence of warning labels: CAUTION, WARNING, and/or DANGER

   - hazardous characteristics: toxic, flammable, explosive, caustic, and/or irritant

   - summary of precautions for using or disposing of the product

Students should perform this activity at school. Have the students record their findings and share them with the class.

2. You are using a hazardous substance if the product label contains the words CAUTION, WARNING, or DANGER. Hazardous substances generally have at least one of the following labels:

   - *toxic:* poisonous, causing physical harm if inhaled, ingested, or absorbed; long-term effects may include cancer or birth defects

   - *flammable:* can catch fire or ignite easily

   - *explosive:* can explode if exposed to shock, heat, or pressure

   - *caustic:* corrosive, burning living tissue on contact

   - *irritant:* can cause skin, eye, or other irritations and inflammation on contact

This question may be answered by students working in small groups, or it may be discussed by the class.

3. After completing your survey, compare your data with that of other students. Which categories of products seem to be the most hazardous? Explain.

   Answers will vary with the products surveyed. Oven cleaners and drain openers are

   among the most hazardous products. The most hazardous products are those com-

   posed of strong bases or acids, chemicals that can cause injury or illness even in low

   concentrations.

   _____

   _____

   _____

   _____

4. When you use hazardous products, it is important to take certain precautions to protect human health and the environment. Read the following safety guidelines, and write down why you think each one is important.

a. Leave hazardous products in their original containers.

Labels on original containers provide information about the contents, including precautions for safe use and disposal; another container might be more easily corroded or damaged.

b. Keep hazardous products in well-ventilated areas, out of the reach of children or pets, and away from heat or sparks.

Ventilation helps prevent the buildup of fumes in storage areas. Children and pets may be harmed unknowingly by hazardous products. Heat or sparks may ignite flammable substances or cause explosions.

c. Always use hazardous products in well-ventilated areas, and wear protective clothing if the product label tells you to.

Ventilation reduces the chance of inhaling toxic fumes. Proper clothing protects your skin from irritants and caustic substances.

d. NEVER dispose of hazardous products by pouring them into storm drains or onto the ground.

Products poured into storm drains often travel directly into waterways and pollute them; they may pollute groundwater used for drinking.

e. NEVER mix hazardous products together.

Hazardous products contain powerful chemicals that may react with each other when mixed, causing dangerous fumes or explosions.

TRY AN ALTERNATIVE

5. Select some common household objects that need cleaning. Prepare an appropriate, less-hazardous cleaning product according to the instructions in the table on the next page.

You may want to ask students to bring soiled items from home for cleaning, or you may supply them. Possible soiled items include stained porcelain dishes; stained wood objects or small pieces of wood furniture (a magazine rack, for instance) in need of polishing; grease-encrusted metal baking or broiling pans; grease-stained cloth; soiled white cloth. Some students may wash the inside of the classroom windows. Alternatively, students could complete steps 5 and 6 at home.

Different groups may choose different alternative product "recipes" and compare their effectiveness at the same cleaning task.

Recipes for Alternative Cleansers			
Drain opener	Pour 1 cup baking soda into drain, then add 1/2 cup warm white vinegar; cover drain for 1 min; rinse with cold water.	**Porcelain cleaner**	Rub on paste of borax and lemon juice; let sit for 2 hr; scrub with nylon scrubber and baking soda paste or cream of tartar paste.
Window cleaner	Mix 1/4 cup white vinegar in 1 qt water; spray on, and wipe with dry newspaper.	**Laundry stain remover**	To remove grease: rub chalk into the affected area, let sit for 15 min, then wash. To remove soil from whites: soak item in baking soda and water solution.
Oven cleaner	Fill spray bottle with equal parts ammonia and water; spray on, close door, and let set for 15 min; wipe off.	**Wood-furniture polish**	Mix 2 tbsp olive oil and 1 tbsp white vinegar, and slowly stir into 1 qt water. Apply to wood, and rub with cloth rag.

6. Test the alternative cleaning product on the soiled item. Continue to apply and use the product until the item is as clean as possible.

7. How effective was the alternative product?

   Answers will vary depending on the nature of the stain or soil that students attempt to remove.

Discuss with students what makes alternative products work and what makes them less hazardous than many commercial products. Some alternative products rely on the properties of acids and bases, some use absorbent properties, and some use abrasive properties. Alternative drain opener generates gases and heat to help break up grease and other materials. Abrasives like baking soda or cream of tartar aren't as harsh as commercial abrasives, but they still help remove soil with friction. Because the alternative products are much weaker, less-ionizing acids and bases than those often contained in commercial products, they are less hazardous to use and to dispose of.

8. What kinds of chemical reactions do you think took place when you used the alternative cleansers?

   Acid and base reactions took place with lemon juice, vinegar, baking soda and washing soda. Baking soda, chalk, and cream of tartar absorb stains.

9. Do you think you have to use more or less mechanical force when using alternative cleansers than with commercial cleansers? Explain your answer.

   In most cases the use of alternative product requires more mechanical force (physical effort) because the acids and bases are weaker and the abrasives are not as harsh.

10. What are the advantages to using alternative cleansers instead of store-bought cleaning products?

   You may use alternative products to avoid health hazards, to avoid storage and disposal difficulties, or to reduce the risk to the environment.

INVESTIGATION

13.1

WATCH A POPULATION GROW

What keeps our population from overrunning the Earth? You learned in Chapter 13 that populations increase exponentially until limiting factors reduce their growth rate. What are these limiting factors? Can they be overcome? In this Investigation, you will observe the growth of yeast in a closed system in order to better understand the factors that limit population growth.

MATERIALS
- molasses
- water
- 100 mL graduated cylinder
- stirring rod
- 100 mL beaker
- microscope
- microscope slides with coverslips
- capillary pipet (or eye-dropper)
- yeast solution

A single yeast cell

A bud begins to form.

The bud grows.

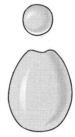
The new bud breaks away from the original cell.

Groups of 3 to 4 students work well for this activity.

To prepare the yeast solution, add 1 g of dry baker's yeast to 100 mL of warm water.

When counting yeast cells, count the buds from asexual reproduction as well as the parent cells.

THE COUNTDOWN

1. Prepare a yeast culture medium by combining 45 mL of water and 5 mL of molasses in a 100 mL beaker. Stir the solution thoroughly.

2. Start a yeast culture by adding 10 drops of yeast solution to the culture medium.

3. Stir your yeast culture to evenly distribute the yeast cells; then immediately dip a capillary pipette into the beaker to collect a small quantity of yeast culture. Place one or two generous drops of yeast culture in the center of a microscope slide.

4. Gently cover the yeast culture with a coverslip.

5. Position the slide on your microscope. Use low power for focusing on the cells, and then switch to high power. Keep the light source dim so that you can see the cells more easily.

If available, hematocytometers provide an easier method of counting cells.

6. Count the number of yeast cells visible in the microscope's field of view under high power. Record the number of cells in the table below. Move the slide slightly, and repeat the count. Repeat two more times, recording your results in the table each time.

7. Calculate the average of your four cell counts. Calculate the average for the entire class. Record these averages in the table on the next page.

If needed, remind students how to calculate averages. Have all students record their daily averages on a master table posted in the classroom, and assign one student to calculate the class average each day.

			Yeast Cell Count			
Day	Observation 1	Observation 2	Observation 3	Observation 4	Average of 4 observations	Class average
0						
1						
2						
3						
4						
5						
6						
7						
8						
9						
10						

8. Repeat steps 3–7 each day for 10 days. Record your results in the table above. If a weekend or holiday prevents you from observing your culture for a day or two, indicate days when cell counts were unavailable.

   If the cells are too numerous to count, dilute a sample of the culture by combining 20 drops (about 1 mL) of culture with 9 mL of water in a test tube prior to counting. Multiply your cell count by 10 before recording it. If the population is still too dense, dilute further by combining 20 drops of the diluted culture with another 9 mL of water, and then multiply the count by 100.

9. Make a line graph showing the growth of your yeast population over time. Also graph the class-average values. In your graphs, remember to show a gap for any days when cultures were not observed.

EXPLOSIVE RESULTS?

10. How did the yeast population change over the course of 10 days? Why do you think this happened?

   The population increased and then decreased. The yeast grew until they started

   running out of food, overcrowding occurred, and waste accumulated.

   _____

   _____

11. What factors could limit a population in nature?

Overcrowded habitat, predation, availability of food, disease, increased waste, and

scarcity of mates are some of the factors that often limit populations.

12. Is the human population controlled by the same limiting factors that you listed above? Why or why not?

The human population can be limited by all of the same factors. However, humans

can overcome many of these limiting factors by developing more efficient food pro-

duction methods, curing diseases, and treating wastes.

PUSHING THE LIMITS

13. How do you think increasing the food supply of the yeast would affect the population curve? Write a hypothesis below.

Sample hypothesis: Increasing the food supply will allow the yeast population to

continue increasing for a longer period of time.

More advanced students could develop hypotheses and design experiments that relate to other factors which limit population growth.

14. Design an experiment to test the effect of increasing the food supply of the yeast. Write out your procedure below, being sure to explain how you will control all variables other than food supply.

Sample experiment: Set up and observe the yeast culture as before. Every two days,

add 1 mL of molasses to the culture. If this causes a noticeable increase in culture

volume, remove an appropriate amount of culture, removing as few yeast cells as

possible. If the volume of the culture decreases due to evaporation, add water to

bring it back to about 50 mL.

_____

_____

_____

_____

_____

_____

15. After your teacher has approved your experimental design, carry out your experiment. Record and graph your data on a separate sheet of paper.

16. How did your yeast population graph differ when you increased the food supply? Was your hypothesis supported?

The curve continues increasing for a longer period of time, but eventually declines.

_____

_____

_____

17. Why is increasing food production only a temporary solution to the human overpopulation problem?

It doesn't solve the other problems associated with overpopulation, such as pollution,

disease, resource depletion, waste accumulation, and overcrowding.

_____

_____

INVESTIGATION 13.2

POPPING POPULATIONS

The growth of natural populations is usually limited by resources, such as food and water, and by predators. However, when populations are not limited, they can grow surprisingly quickly. This is because each successive generation is larger than the last, yet each generation reproduces in the same amount of time.

Although all organisms are capable of exponential growth, it is usually only possible to observe rapid population growth in organisms that are small enough to find sufficient space and nutrients. For example, we can observe the exponential growth of a population of bacteria by putting a few bacteria in a large flask containing a nutrient-rich broth. The bacteria's population will increase exponentially, and the broth will become cloudy with bacteria in just a few days. A graph of this population's growth rate is shaped like a "J." Eventually, the bacteria will exhaust the limited space and nutrients. Once this happens, the population will "crash."

In this activity, you will simulate the exponential growth of a population. First, you will use a popcorn popper to "grow" a population of popcorn. Then you will use a computer to model and graph population growth.

CREATE A POPCORN POPULATION

1. Fill the air popper measuring cup to the top with popcorn. Level off the kernels with your hand.

2. STOP! Before you continue, read steps 3–7. Once the popcorn begins to pop, you will need to be prepared and ready to collect data.

3. Turn on the popper and pour in the popcorn kernels. The air popper may work better if it runs for 2–3 minutes before the popcorn is added. Place a bowl under the spout of the air popper to catch the popcorn.

4. As soon as the first popped kernel falls into the bowl, start the stopwatch, remove the bowl, and replace the bowl with an empty one. Every 15 seconds, remove the bowl under the popper spout and put another bowl under the spout. Keep track of the order in which the bowls are removed.

5. Continue to collect and set aside the popcorn every 15 seconds until all of the popcorn is popped. Turn off the popper.

Groups of 3 students work well for this activity.

A few popped kernels will collect in the popper before beginning to fall into the bowl. This amount will have a negligible effect on the overall lab results.

Number the bowls from 1 to 15. Make sure to use each bowl in numerical order to catch the popcorn. Each bowl will represent a generation. Make sure that the bowls are large enough to allow for the "exponential" growth that will occur in each generation.

INVESTIGATION 13.2, CONTINUED

Students should count the popcorn one generation at a time. Have them empty one bowl, count the popped kernels, and return the popcorn to the bowl before counting the popcorn in the next bowl. This will prevent mixing up the generations.

If more room is needed to record the generations, continue the table to the left on a piece of graph paper.

6. Determine the population by counting the number of the kernels in each bowl. Record the data in the table below.

Popcorn Population Growth					
Time (seconds)	Bowl number	Number of kernels	Time (seconds)	Bowl number	Number of kernels
15	1		135	9	
30	2		150	10	
45	3		165	11	
60	4		180	12	
75	5		195	13	
90	6		210	14	
105	7		225	15	
120	8				

Discuss with students the forces at work that would influence these population numbers. Ask students to describe the population growth characterized by each generation. For example, a rapidly growing generation could be a result of a newly exploited food source or the sudden elimination of a predator or disease.

7. Describe the population growth recorded in the chart. What forces would allow for this kind of growth in a population of organisms?

Answers will vary. This is an example of exponential growth because the population

grows successively larger with each generation until the resource base (kernels) is

depleted.

_____

8. On the next page, graph the relationship between elapsed time and population using your results. Plot each generation with the time popped on the horizontal (x) axis and the number of kernels per bowl on the vertical (y) axis. Draw a line connecting the points. Describe the shape of the line. What does this tell you about the population growth?

Answers will vary, but the line will probably form a J-curve initially as the popcorn

population grows exponentially. The population will then "crash" and suddenly curve

down as the popcorn popper runs out of kernels.

_____

_____

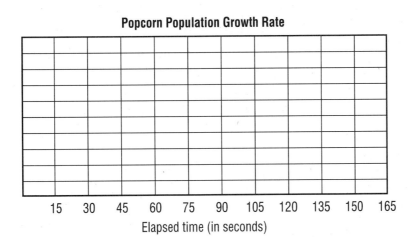

Popcorn Population Growth Rate

Elapsed time (in seconds)

15 30 45 60 75 90 105 120 135 150 165

If students need more space, suggest they plot the generations on graph paper.

ANALYZE YOUR RESULTS

9. Describe what happened to your population at progressive time intervals.

As the number of elapsed intervals increased, the population increased.

10. Does popping popcorn realistically model an exponentially growing population? Explain your answer.

Yes and no; popping popcorn replicates the dynamics, or look, of an exponentially growing population. The population grows slowly at first, and then growth accelerates. Also, the population almost doubles in each generation. Popping popcorn is not a realistic model because it doesn't replicate the underlying mechanisms of population growth. The popcorn is not actually reproducing. And even with space (storage) limitations, the popcorn will continue to pop until all poppable kernels are gone.

Discuss how exponential growth occurs. In the absence of predation or disease, the population exponentially grows to the limits of the resource base. In this activity, the unpopped kernels represent both the source of the growing generations and their resource base. When all the kernels have popped, the population levels off.

11. Assume that fresh popcorn kernels pop much more readily than stale kernels. Would stale kernels be useful for simulating nonexponential growth? Why?

A lot of the stale popcorn would not pop. This would mean that the population would not grow exponentially, so it would look more like a normal population increase.

Name_____ Class_____ Date _____

QBasic is not available for Macintosh computers, but Chipmunk Basic, which is similar to QBasic, is available as shareware for the Macintosh.

MAKE A COMPUTER SIMULATION

12. We can simulate population growth on a computer or with a few keystrokes on a graphing calculator. Skip to step 15 if you are using a graphing calculator. With an IBM-compatible computer, start at the DOS prompt. Type "QBasic" and press <enter> to start the application. Enter this program:

```
x = 1
CLS
BEGIN:
CLS
x = x + 1
y = 2^x
FOR n = 1 to y
PRINT "x";
NEXT n
INPUT m
GOTO BEGIN
```

13. The Xs on the screen represent organisms. Does this program realistically model exponential population growth? Explain your answer.

Yes and no; it shows the potential for a population to grow exponentially, but it is not

realistic to expect actual populations to show such a perfect increase.

14. Use the following program to generate the number of organisms in each generation of an exponentially growing population.

```
x = 1
CLS
BEGIN:
x = x + 1
y = 2^x
PRINT y
INPUT m
GOTO BEGIN
```

The keystrokes entered in step 15 are for the algebraic formula:

$$y_1 = 2\,(2^x)$$

where x equals the generation number and y equals the population in that generation.

15. Next plot the growth of your simulated population on graph paper or on a graphing calculator. If you use a graphing calculator, generate the graph by entering: 2×2^x or $2(2^x)$ into the calculator. What happens to the population in each successive generation?

The population doubled.

16. Compare the graphs of the popcorn population and the virtual population.

Both graphs illustrate exponential growth. Both graphs show the population growing

slowly at first and then increasing rapidly.

INVESTIGATION 13.3

SO MANY PEOPLE!

In the last few decades the human population has doubled. In the decades ahead it will double again. The human population has grown so quickly that many fear we are at a crisis point. Indeed, many environmental problems occur simply because there are so many people.

The human population is growing unevenly throughout the world. In many developed countries, the population is growing very slowly or even declining. But in the less-developed parts of the world the population is growing at a significant rate. In a few countries, particularly the very poorest, the population is growing quite rapidly.

In this Investigation you will use census data to determine the growth rate of your community. Using this growth rate, you will estimate the growth of your community over the next few decades. Then, you will compute the population growth of your community using several hypothetical growth rates. Finally, you will project the future populations of the United States and the world based on their actual current growth rates.

MATERIALS

- almanac (containing census data) or statistical census abstract
- calculator (scientific model)

Groups of 2 to 4 students work well for this activity. Be sure each group has at least one student with strong math skills.

Most libraries will have census and statistical information that students can use.

PROCEDURE

1. Use reference sources to determine the population of your community (or one nearby) in two recent successive years. Use the two most recent years available. If references do not contain this information or are unavailable, you can probably obtain the information from your Chamber of Commerce or city hall.

2. Use the population data to determine the growth rate of your community. The procedure for doing this is shown in the box on the next page.

3. Record your population information.

   a. population in the first year? _____ Answers to questions 3 and 4 will vary. Students

   b. population the following year? _____ should use the growth rate formula provided in

   c. growth rate in percent? _____ the box on the next page.

4. Based on this growth rate, what will the population be 5 years from the first year for which you obtained census data? _Answers will vary._____

   10 years? _____ 20 years? _____ 50 years? _____ 100 years? _____

5. Are each of the population projections you calculated in step 4 likely to be equally accurate? Why or why not?

   The long-range growth forecasts (20 years or more) are probably most inaccurate

   because it is unlikely that the growth rate would remain constant over a long period

   of time.

INVESTIGATION 13.3, CONTINUED

Sample problem

2011 population: 100,000

2012 population: 104,000

Find the growth rate, and then use this growth rate to calculate the population 5 years from the year 2012.

Solution

Growth rate = second year population ÷ first year population

Growth rate = 104,000 ÷ 100,000 = 1.04

To change the growth rate to a percentage, subtract 1 then multiply by 100.

1.04 − 1 = 0.04; 0.04 × 100 = 4

Growth rate in percent = 4%

The following formula allows you to compute growth over multiple years.

Final population = initial population × (growth rate)^y,
where y is the number of years over which growth takes place.

You will need a calculator that can compute exponents to use this formula. Most scientific calculators are capable of this. If you do not have such a calculator, you will have to multiply the growth rate by itself for each year of growth.

Population in 2017 = 104,000 × (1.04)^5 = 126,532.

(Round to the nearest whole number.)

Growth rates expressed as percentages must be changed back to their original form in order to be used in the growth formula. To do this, divide by 100, and then add 1.00.

6. Calculate your city's growth over the next 100 years using the following hypothetical annual growth rates: 0.25 percent, 2 percent, and 4 percent. Graph your results in the space provided on the following page. Compute the data for 10 year intervals. Finish your calculations before you fill in the graph. But before you start calculating, make a prediction about the rate at which population will increase for each growth rate. For example, you might say "The population will increase twice as fast with a 4 percent growth rate as with a 2 percent growth rate" or "The population will double in 25 years with a 4 percent growth rate."

What is your prediction? __Accept all reasonable predictions.__

_____

_____

7. In recent years, the population of the United States has increased by about 1 percent per year. Assuming a present population of 275 million and a constant growth rate, what will the population be in the year 2010? _____

2020? _____ 2050? _____ 2100? _____

Assuming a start time of 2000: 2010, 304 million; 2020, 335 million; 2050, 452 million; 2100, 744 million

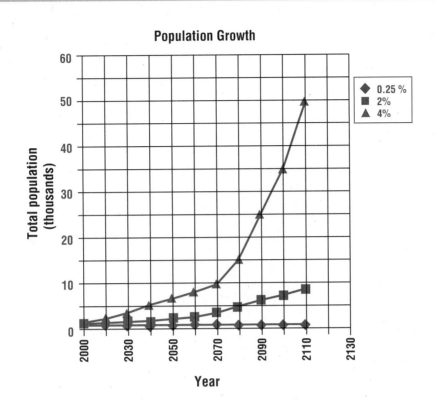

The sample graph shown here is based on a starting population of 2,000.

8. The world's population is increasing by about 1.8 percent per year. Assuming a current population of 5.9 billion and a constant growth rate, what will the population be in 2050? _____ 2100? _____

Assuming a start time of 2000: 2050, 14.4 billion; 2100, 35.2 billion

THINK ABOUT IT

9. What kind of problems, if any, is your community likely to experience if its current rate of growth continues indefinitely? Explain.

Answers will vary but should mention a strained infrastructure, housing shortages,

increased traffic, damage to the environment, pollution, etc.

_____

_____

_____

_____

_____

_____

10. Would it be realistic to project the world population in the year 2300 based on today's growth rates? Why or why not?

   No, it would not be realistic. If today's growth rate were sustained through the year

   2300, the population would be somewhere around 1.25 trillion people—a population

   too large for Earth to support. As more and more of the world's countries become

   developed, their birth rates are likely to drop.

   _____

   _____

   _____

11. It has been said that "humans must solve their population problem or nature will solve it for them." What do you think is meant by this?

   If people do not control their own population, the carrying capacity of the planet may

   eventually be exceeded. As happens in other populations that have exceeded their

   environment's carrying capacity, famines, epidemics, and other disasters may elimi-

   nate the "excess" population.

   _____

   _____

   _____

INVESTIGATION 13.4

PEBBLE MARK-RECAPTURE

One popular and simple technique for estimating a wild population of animals is called the *mark-recapture method*. It works like this: Suppose that you want to estimate the population of goldfish in a pond. You catch, tag, and release 40 fish. A few days later, you catch 40 fish and notice that 10 of the fish were tagged from the first catch—in other words, they were recaptured. To estimate the population of fish in the pond (N), multiply the number of fish in the first sample (M) by the number in the second sample (n), and divide the product by the number of "recaptures" (R).

$$N = \frac{Mn}{R} = \frac{\text{(first sample)} \times \text{(second sample)}}{\text{number recaptured}} = \text{estimated population}$$

To estimate the fish population,

$$\frac{40 \times 40}{10} = \frac{1600}{10} = 160$$

Therefore, the estimated number of goldfish in the pond is 160. For the estimate to be accurate, you need to sample a fairly large population, and at least one animal must be captured in each sample. In general, the bigger your samples, the more accurate your estimate.

USE THE FORMULA

1. You are an entomologist (a scientist who studies insects) trying to determine the population of Japanese beetles in your backyard. Two weeks ago you captured, marked, and released 100 beetles. Yesterday, you caught 40 beetles; 20 were recaptured from the first sample. Estimate the Japanese beetle population in your backyard. Show your work.

N = 100 × 40 /20 = 200; The estimated population is 200 beetles.

STALK THE WILD PEBBLE

2. Fill the jar half-way with pebbles. These pebbles represent a population of wild animals. Do not count the pebbles.

MATERIALS
- 1 qt. jar
- pebbles
- 2 shades of colored nail polish

You may want to substitute pennies for pebbles.

The actual population should number at least 100.

3. Remove a handful of pebbles from the jar. The handful represents your first sample of animals. Count the pebbles, and write the total on the line below. Paint each pebble in your sample with a drop of nail polish. After the polish dries, return the pebbles to the jar and thoroughly mix them with the others.

Answers will vary.

4. Remove another handful of pebbles from the jar, and record the total below.

Answers will vary.

5. Count and record the number of pebbles that were "recaptured."

Answers will vary.

6. Use the formula to estimate the number of pebbles in the jar. Write your estimation on the line below. The formula is as follows:

$$\boxed{N = \frac{Mn}{R}} = \frac{\text{(first sample)} \times \text{(second sample)}}{\text{number recaptured}} = \text{estimated population}$$

Answers will vary.

7. Repeat steps 2–6 with the same jar of pebbles but use a different color of nail polish. Record your data below.

Number in first sample = **Answers will vary.**

Number in second sample = **Answers will vary.**

Number recaptured = **Answers will vary.**

Estimated population = **Answers will vary.**

8. Count the total number of pebbles in the jar. Record the number below.

Answers will vary.

9. Compare the actual number of pebbles with the estimates in steps 6 and 7.

The actual number will probably be close but not identical to the estimated numbers.

10. Based on what you observed in this exercise, do you think that the mark-recapture method is a good way to estimate population? Explain your answer.

Answers will vary.

INVESTIGATION 13.4, CONTINUED

EVALUATE THE METHOD

11. Imagine two ponds, one large and one small. You catch, tag, and release 20 goldfish from each pond. The next day, you catch 20 goldfish from each pond and count 8 recaptures from the small pond and 2 from the large pond.

a. Estimate the population of goldfish in the small pond.

20 × 20 ÷ 8 = 50

b. Estimate the population of goldfish in the large pond.

20 × 20 ÷ 2 = 200

c. Why would a large pond tend to have fewer recaptures than a small pond?

The large pond can support more fish, so there will be a wider range of possible

fish to recatch, reducing the chances of recapturing any one fish.

12. Which of the following examples do you think reflects the largest population? Which reflects the smallest? Explain your answer.
a. large first sample, large second sample, large recapture
b. large first sample, large second sample, small recapture
c. small first sample, large second sample, large recapture
d. small first sample, small second sample, large recapture

If students have difficulty understanding the reasoning, they can plug in sample numbers for each example:

a. 50, 50, 40

b. 50, 50, 10

c. 25, 50, 30

d. 25, 25, 20

B reflects the largest population because there were two large captures and a

small number of recaptured individuals. Fewer recaptures indicate a larger popu-

lation. D reflects the smallest population because few individuals were captured,

and of those that were, many were recaptured. Few captures and a high number of

recaptures indicate a small population.

13. a. If you captured, marked, and released 5 turtles from a pond, and caught 10 unmarked turtles the next day, would you have enough information to estimate the population using the mark-recapture method?

No; the mark-recapture method requires at least one recaptured animal. Also, the

sample is too small to get an accurate estimate of the population.

b. If you captured and marked one turtle from a pond and captured the same turtle the next day, can you conclude that only one turtle lives in the pond? Explain your answer.

According to the mark-recapture method, there is an estimated population of one

turtle living in the pond. However, there may be other turtles in the pond that

were not captured. For the estimate to be accurate, there must be a larger num-

ber of turtles in the samples.

14. Imagine that you are studying birds that are flying south for the winter. How might their migration affect the results of a mark-recapture study? Can you accurately estimate the migrating bird population using the mark-recapture method? Explain your answer?

If animals are migrating, the number of recaptures should be very low, making popu-

lation estimates unrealistically high. It is difficult to accurately estimate the popula-

tion of any moving population. The mark-recapture method works best with

populations which are relatively stationary.

Students have the opportunity to apply the mark-recapture method in the field by completing Investigation 13.1 in the *Field Activities and Projects Guide* booklet.

INVESTIGATION 14.1

THE PRISONER'S DILEMMA

The most pressing environmental problems, such as the loss of biodiversity and stratospheric ozone, are international in nature. The solution to these problems does not lie with one group or nation. Instead it ultimately depends on cooperation—between people, between businesses, and between governments. However, there are often advantages to not cooperating, or cheating, if you can get away with it. For example, once several nations agree to each reduce pollution by adopting expensive but environmentally friendly production methods, cheating becomes very attractive. By ignoring the expensive restrictions, a country can make more products for less money, so businesses stay profitable and citizens stay employed. It may be wrong to cheat on environmental agreements, but the financial and political incentives to do so are there.

In this activity, you will explore cooperation by playing a game. The game is derived from a story problem called "The Prisoner's Dilemma." Here is the story: Two suspects are arrested and placed in separate cells, where they cannot communicate with one another. The police urge each suspect to confess, but the suspects know that without a confession the police have a weak case. Of course each suspect hopes to go free. Knowing this, the police devise a plan. If one suspect confesses and provides evidence against the other, that suspect will go free and the other will get a harsh sentence. If both suspects confess, the police will give both suspects a moderate sentence because although they are guilty they were also honest. If neither suspect confesses, both suspects will receive a light sentence because the police lack evidence for a strong case. Each suspect must guess what the other suspect will do and act accordingly. Parties to an environmental agreement are faced with the same dilemma as these suspects are—to cheat or not to cheat?

Possible outcomes of
The Prisoner's Dilemma

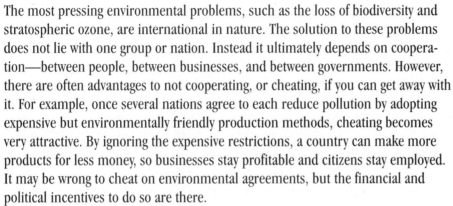

P1 = Prisoner 1
P2 = Prisoner 2

Groups of 2 students work well for this activity.

The book *Can You Win?* by Mike Orkin (NY: 1991) W. H. Freeman and Co., includes an excellent treatment of the prisoner's dilemma and its possible outcomes.

CONSIDER THE DILEMMA

1. What do you think each suspect should do? What do you think each suspect will do? Explain your answer.

   Answers will vary. There is a big incentive to cheat, so one or both of the prisoners

   will probably cheat. Cooperation makes better sense for the benefit of both parties,

   but the prisoners may risk the longer sentence for the chance to go free without

   penalty.

AN ENVIRONMENTAL "PRISONER'S DILEMMA"

Imagine that you make your living fishing in an area of the sea that lies within international waters. Because of overfishing, the population of fish in the area has drastically declined in recent years. In the past you were able to keep as much as you caught, sometimes up to 300 fish a day. Fishing is now regulated by an international agreement that prohibits anyone from catching more than 100 fish per day. This will give the population a chance to regenerate.

In order to be allowed to continue fishing, you have agreed to abide by this limit. The other people fishing in this area have agreed to this limit as well. There are now penalties for overfishing, but the chances of getting caught are slight. It is tempting to cheat on the agreement by catching more fish in order to make a better living. If you do cheat, you will probably not have any problems at first, but the other people fishing in your area may have a smaller catch as a result of your overfishing.

Long-term consequences may be difficult for the students to grasp, especially when the short-term gain is so obvious. Discuss how the decisions to cheat or co-operate will affect the fish population, and the people who make their living by fishing.

2. There are obvious benefits to cheating on this agreement. But are the long-term consequences worth it?

   Answers will vary. Long-term consequences could be that the fish population

   declines so severely that the fishing industry itself is threatened and the individual,

   although gaining a better living in the short term, loses that livelihood altogether in

   the long term.

3. Assume that you have agreed to cooperate with a partner on resolving this environmental problem. Why should both parties agree to cooperate?

   The actions of each party affect the shared environment of both parties. If one party

   cheats, the other suffers. Ultimately both parties will be harmed by cheating on the

   agreement because poor environmental quality effects everyone.

4. What things are necessary for any international environmental agreement to be successful?

   Students may list mutual trust, dedication to a higher cause (Earth's survival), international monitoring, or severe penalties in the case of cheating.

   _____

   _____

PLAY THE GAME

5. Play a game modeled on this environmental problem. Divide into pairs. Without consulting the other player, choose whether to cooperate (abide by the fishing agreement) or to cheat. Write your decision ("cooperate" or "cheat") on a slip of paper. Compare your answer with what your partner has decided.

6. Each player begins the game with 10 points. Score each round of play in the following manner. Record your score in the table below.

- If both players choose to cooperate, each earns 1 point.

- If both players cheat, they each lose 2 points.

- If one player cooperates and one cheats, the cheater earns 5 points while the cooperative player loses 3 points.

Environmental Dilemma: Scoring Chart				
	Player 1		Player 2	
	Cheat	Cooperate	Cheat	Cooperate
Round 1				
Round 2				
Round 3				
Round 4				
Round 5				
Round 6				
Round 7				
Round 8				
Total Score				

7. How many times did cheating happen in this game for your group?

<u>Answers will vary.</u>

8. Now adjust your score according to your teacher's instructions. How many points did you end with in the game?

<u>Answers will vary.</u>

The initial 10 points represent each student's stake in the resource base.

A small incentive is given for cooperating, although in many environmental agreements there are no obvious incentives to keep the agreement other than to avoid penalties for cheating.

If both players cheat at the same time, they each lose points because the shared resource (fish) is getting exhausted that much faster, harming both parties equally.

If one player cheats while the other cooperates, the cheater gets the most resources while suffering no immediate consequences. The cooperative party loses the most in this case and gains nothing, absorbing instead the impact of the cheater's actions.

The object of the exercise is to illustrate the incentives to cooperate and to cheat. The short-term benefits of cheating are obvious from the points accumulated by strategic cheating.

In order to illustrate the long-term consequences of cheating on environmental agreements, penalize each group for their total occurrences of cheating (not the total points accumulated from cheating). After the first five occurrences of cheating in a group, penalize the group by taking away 10 points from each person's score. Also take away a point for every other occurrence of cheating.

Have each group compare initial and final scores. How do the scores vary? Discuss the meaning of these scores.

9. Although both parties stand to benefit if each party cooperates on the agreement, cheating provides an opportunity for individual gain at a cost to the other party. Well-timed cheating builds your point count much faster than cooperation alone. Cheating, however, invites retaliation, which then lowers both players' scores.

Did you use a strategy when you played the game? If so, what was your strategy, and did it depend on what your opponent did?

All but the most disinterested student should have had some plan for the game. For

example, "I always cooperated because even if they cheat, the Earth will benefit from

my behavior," would be an acceptable answer.

10. Is this game a realistic model of the possible difficulties involved in enforcing international environmental treaties? Explain your answer.

Students should recognize the devastating effect cheating has on agreements based

on mutual cooperation.

11. How might the game be modified to prevent cheating or make it less attractive? Are there any ways these modifications could be applied to international agreements in the real world?

Common suggestions will probably be to eliminate the bonus for cheating, to intro-

duce a referee to prevent cheating, and to insert a clause punishing cheaters.

12. Not all agreements are bilateral (between just two sides). How might you modify the rules of the game to allow for three or more participants (multilateral agreements)? What might you need to change? Remember, the game should still be a good model; similar actions in the game and in the real world have similar rewards and risks.

This provides an extension for the student who is really interested in this type of

game or analysis. If worked on for an extended time, the game can become as com-

plex as life itself. Some students may also want to develop a board or computer

game based on this work.

As simple as it seems, this game has been studied as a way to analyze everything from union negotiations to nuclear disarmament talks. The most rewarding strategy depends on how long the game is played. For a single round, cheating is the only smart decision. However, if one must play repeatedly, any number of strategies are viable.

Some possible strategies include:

Blind cooperation: Cooperate no matter what.

Tit for tat: Do not cheat unless the other person does, and then only when they do. (This will probably be the most frequently used strategy.)

Vindictive: Cooperate until the other player cheats, and then cheat from there on out.

Cheat if behind; cooperate if ahead.

Cheat for two turns after the other player cheats, and then cooperate thereafter.

Discuss these strategies in terms of real-world scenarios in which the results of decisions to cheat or to cooperate are usually less clearly defined.

T E X T   I N V E S T I G A T I O N

AN ONION CONUNDRUM

1. Scientific Problem: ___Why Omar's onions did not take root_____

_____

2. Variables: ___Possible variables include the amount of water, the amount of organic fertilizer, and the__

___amount of bleach in the groundwater underneath the farm._____

Hypothesis: ___Sample hypothesis: The onions failed to take root because the new watering system did not pro-__

___vide the onions with adequate moisture._____

4. How much of each substance will you use? ___Accept all reasonable answers._____

_____

What will your sample size be? ___Sample size may vary but should consist of at least two onions for each__

___experimental condition._____

Is it necessary to set up a control? Why or why not? ___A control is necessary because it provides a standard__

___against which change can be measured._____

Make a complete list of your procedures on a separate sheet of paper.

6. Record your data in the table. If you use more than three test tubes, make a table on a separate sheet of paper to record additional data. Make a line graph of the data in the space on the next page.

Day	Length of Roots (cm)		
	Solution A: _____	Solution B: _____	Solution C: _____
1	Data will vary.		
2			
3			
4			
5			

Onion Growth in Test Solutions

Length of roots (cm) *(y-axis)*

Day *(x-axis)* 0 1 2 3 4 5

7. Write your report on a separate sheet of paper.

8. Variable changed: __Sample answer for the hypothesis listed in item 2: The amount of water is the variable__

__that was changed.__

Variables held constant: __All variables except the water remained constant.__

Why is it important to change only one variable? __Changing only one variable is necessary to identify__

__clearly the factor that is inhibiting the growth of the roots.__

9. Describe an experiment you could do to test the effect of another variable on plant growth.

__To test the effects of acid rain or salt accumulation on the onion bulbs, students could use the procedure__

__outlined in this Investigation and incorporate solutions of varying levels of acidity or salinity.__

T E X T   I N V E S T I G A T I O N ②

SHOWDOWN ON THE PRAIRIE

2. What is the purpose of the control pots? **They provide information on the growth that can be expected in the** **absence of competition from the other species; they are also useful for identifying the species in the mixed pot.**

_____

3. Hypothesis: **Sample hypothesis: Growth will be impaired by the presence of another species.**

_____

_____

5. Record your data in the table. Use a separate sheet of paper for more data if needed.

| | Species A Alone | | Species B Alone | | Plants in Mixed Pot | | | |
| | | | | | Species A | | Species B | |
	Max. height	No. of leaves	Max. height	No. of leaves	Max. height	No. of leaves	Max. height	No. of leaves
Day 1								
Day 2								
Day 3								
Day 4								
Day 5								
Day 6								
Day 7								

6. Graph your data on a separate sheet of paper.

7. How did the growth of each species in the absence of competition differ from its growth in the presence of competition?

Answers will vary; usually, one or both of the two species will grow less in the presence of a competitor than it will **by itself.**

_____

Did the experiment support your hypothesis? **Answers will vary. Student answers should provide a clear and** **concise interpretation of the results.**

8. Why is it difficult to simulate competition in the laboratory? Lab conditions will not mimic exactly conditions in the wild. For example, temperature may vary a great deal in nature but remain constant in the lab. One species might be better able to survive changes in temperature. Also, predators or other factors may affect growth rates in the wild.

9. Factor to investigate: Accept all reasonable responses.

10. Hypothesis: Answers will vary. Hypotheses should be clear and logical.

11. Record your experimental design on a separate sheet of paper.

12. Prediction: Answers will vary. Predictions should be clear and logical.

13. On a separate sheet of paper, record your results in a data table.

14. Graph the results of your experiment on a separate sheet of paper.

15. Which grass species "won" in your classmates' competition experiments? Answers will vary depending on specific circumstances.

Why might one species outcompete another? As experimental conditions begin to resemble the ideal growing conditions for one of the species, that species should be more successful as a competitor.

16. It is hard to draw conclusions about plant competition based on laboratory experiments because in a laboratory experiment a limited number of variables are examined, while in nature there are usually many more variables that may affect competition among species.

Possible additional experiments: More complex experiments could be performed to test the reactions of several species to several variables in different combinations; also, a field study that examines native soils might be informative.

TEXT INVESTIGATION

WHAT'S IN AN ECOSYSTEM?

5. Kinds of plants and animals observed: _____Answers will vary depending on specific circumstances._____

_____

_____

_____

_____

_____

_____

6. Producers: _____Symbol should indicate plants._____

   Consumers: _____Symbol should indicate animals._____

   Decomposers: _____Symbol should indicate fungi and most soil organisms._____

7. Organisms interacting with each other: _____Answers will vary depending on the particular circumstances, but students should demonstrate the ability to make careful and thorough observations._____

   _____

   Organisms interacting with environment: _____Answers will vary depending on the particular circumstances, but students should demonstrate the ability to make careful and thorough observations._____

   _____

10. Food chains:

    (1) _____Sample answer: grass ⟶ grasshopper ⟶ bird_____

    (2) _____Sample answer: rosebush ⟶ aphid ⟶ ladybug_____

11. Do you expect to find more producers or more consumers? _____producers_____

    Is this what you observed? _____Answers should provide a clear and concise interpretation of observations._____

    _____

    _____

    Explain your observations. _____Sample explanation: Some consumers may draw resources from outside the site, or producers may be small and therefore difficult to observe and count accurately._____

    _____

12. Decomposers observed: _____ Sample answer: mushrooms and other fungi _____

Additional decomposers that might be present: _____ Sample answer: bacteria and fungus spores that are ____

invisible to the naked eye and earthworms and other soil organisms that are probably present underground

13. What role do decomposers play? _____ Decomposers break down rotting organic material into basic, reusable ____

substances.

_____

What would happen if there were no decomposers? _____ Dead organic matter would eventually pile up, and ____

living producers would use up the soil nutrients, leaving the site unable to sustain any life.

_____

14. How are biotic factors affected by abiotic factors? _____ Sample answer: Certain organisms were observed ____

where the sunlight was at its brightest, the soil was dry, and few rocks were present, while others were

observed in shady, moist, rocky areas.

_____

How are abiotic factors affected by biotic factors? _____ Sample answer: By growing, moving, and releasing ____

wastes, living things modify the soil and air, create shade, and affect erosion rates.

_____

_____

15. Question about the ecosystem: _____ Accept all reasonable responses. _____

_____

_____

An experiment or field study to investigate the question: _____ Students might move rocks to a different location ____

to observe the effects on organisms that live under the rocks. Or students could create an area of dense shade

and investigate the effects on the organisms present.

_____

_____

_____

Name_____ Class_____ Date_____

IDENTIFY YOUR LOCAL BIOME

1. Latitude: ___**Answers will vary depending on specific circumstances.**_____

2. Topography: ___**Answers will vary depending on your particular circumstances.**_____

3. Record precipitation and temperature values in the table. Draw your climatogram below.

	Jan.	Feb.	Mar.	Apr.	May	June	July	Aug.	Sept.	Oct.	Nov.	Dec.
Precip. (cm)												
Temp. (°C)												

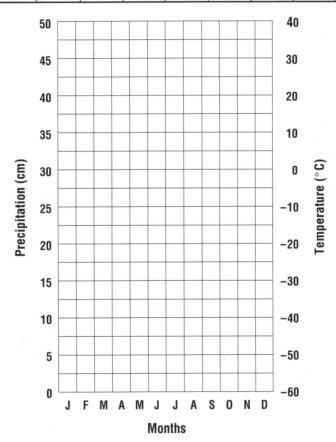

4. Record observations and sketches of plants on a separate sheet of paper.

5. Record observations and sketches of animals on a separate sheet of paper.

6. Biome with most similar climatogram: ___**Answers will vary.**_____

7. Biome that best matches (considering all factors): ___**Answers will vary.**_____

8. How plant adaptations meet conditions of biome:

(1) ___Answers will vary depending on your particular circumstances. Students should be accurate and___

___comprehensive in their responses.___

(2) _____

_____

(3) _____

_____

9. How animal adaptations meet conditions of biome:

(1) ___Answers will vary depending on your particular circumstances. Students should be accurate and___

___comprehensive in their responses.___

(2) _____

_____

(3) _____

_____

10. Does your climatogram match exactly? ___An exact match is unlikely.___

How might these differences affect plant and animal adaptations? ___Answers will vary depending on your___

___particular circumstances. Students should be accurate and comprehensive in their responses. Sample answer:___

___Since our biome gets less rain than the one in the chapter, plants might have more water-conserving adapta-___

___tions like waxy coatings, deep roots, or narrow leaves.___

Could you notice any of those influences? ___Answers will vary.___

_____

_____

11. What features of your biome are created by the organisms that live there?

___Answers will vary depending on your particular circumstances. For example, one of the most obvious features of___

___forest biomes is the habitat created by trees.___

_____

T E X T   I N V E S T I G A T I O N

HOW SAFE IS OUR GROUNDWATER?

3. Record your observations in the table.

Observations of Substances in Surface Water		
Contaminant	**Appearance**	**Measurements (if any)**
Glucose (5 mL)	Observations should be clear and concise.	
Soil (5 mL)		
Food coloring (5 drops)		
Water (control)		

5. Predict how well the filters will clean each water sample.

glucose: ___Sample prediction: Glucose will not be successfully filtered._____

soil: ___Sample prediction: Soil will be successfully filtered._____

food coloring: ___Sample prediction: Food coloring will not be successfully filtered._____

7. Record your observations of the filtered solutions in the table.

Observations of Substances in Groundwater		
Contaminant	**Appearance**	**Measurements (if any)**
Glucose	Observations should be clear and concise.	
Soil		
Food coloring		
Water (control)		

8. Is glucose still present? ___Yes_____

Can you see it? ___No, but it is detectable with test paper._____

9. Was soil removed? How do you know? ___Yes, because it is not visible_____

Was food coloring removed? How do you know? ___No, because it is still visible_____

10. How accurate were your predictions? ___Answers will vary. Students should provide a clear and concise___ interpretation of their results.

Conclusions: ___Students should note that substances that are dissolved in the water (food coloring and glucose) pass through the filter. They may conclude from this observation that any hazardous chemicals that dissolve in water pose a threat to our groundwater sources.___

11. Substance to test: ___Accept all reasonable answers.___

Prediction: ___Answers will vary depending on substance chosen. In most cases, if a substance is a liquid or dissolves in water, it will still be present in the water after filtration.___

Reasons for prediction: ___Answers will vary but should be clear and logical.___

12. Observations of test solution before filtering: ___Observations should be clear and concise.___

Observations of test solution after filtering: ___Observations should be clear and concise.___

How did your results compare with your prediction? ___Students should provide a clear and concise___ interpretation of their results.

13. Conclusions about what types of substances will or will not be filtered out by the earth: ___Sample answer: Water is an excellent solvent, so harmful substances such as fertilizers, insecticides, and hazardous wastes can potentially be carried by water through the ground.___

What precautions do you recommend for keeping groundwater clean? ___Sample answers: recycling motor oil instead of dumping it, minimizing the use of fertilizers and pesticides, and protecting groundwater recharge zones from pollution and hazardous materials___

TEXT INVESTIGATION 6

HOW DOES ACID PRECIPITATION AFFECT PLANTS?

4., 6., 9. Record your observations in the table.

Solution	Appearance of seeds after soaking	Total number of seeds	Number of seeds that germinated	Percentage of seeds that germinated
Water pH = _____	Students should notice that soaking the seeds softens the seed coat.		many	
Acid precipitation pH = _____			few, if any	

10. What was the effect of "acid precipitation" on the seeds? __It should be apparent that the "acid__

__precipitation" prevented the seeds from germinating._____

If a farmer planted 10,000 seeds in soil that had been exposed to acid precipitation, how many plants would he lose?

__Based on student results, the farmer would probably lose all 10,000 plants._____

11. Hypothesis: __Sample hypothesis: Less damage would occur to a plant if its water supply were exposed to__

__limestone._____

12. Record your experimental procedure on a separate sheet of paper.

13. Prediction: __Sample prediction: Germination will occur in the beaker with water only and in the beaker with__

__the artificial acid precipitation and limestone chips._____

14. Record your results in the table. Use a separate sheet of paper for additional data if needed.

Solution	Appearance of seeds after soaking	Total number of seeds	Number of seeds that germinated	Percentage of seeds that germinated
	Data will vary.			

TEXT INVESTIGATION, CONTINUED

Solution	Appearance of seeds after soaking	Total number of seeds	Number of seeds that germinated	Percentage of seeds that germinated

15. Did your results agree with your prediction?   Answers will vary. Student answers should provide a clear and concise interpretation of their results.

Was your hypothesis supported?   Answers will vary. Student answers should provide a clear and concise interpretation of their results.

16. How did your experiment mimic real-world effects?   Sample answer: The results of this experiment show that acid precipitation affects seed germination—this is known to be true in the real world.

How was it different from the real world?   Sample answer: The experiment is not realistic; in nature, seeds would not soak for 24 hours in a pure "acid precipitation" solution. Instead, seeds would probably be in soil, and that soil would probably contain some compounds that could at least partially neutralize the acid.

How could you make your experiment more realistic?   Sample answer: I could grow the seeds in soil.

T E X T   I N V E S T I G A T I O N   7

GLOBAL WARMING IN A JAR

5. Record your data in the table. Use a separate sheet of paper for additional data if needed.

Time	Temperature	
	Uncovered jar (control)	Covered jar ("greenhouse")
Before going outdoors	Data will vary.	
When first placed in sun		
+ 2 minutes		
+ 4 minutes		
+ 6 minutes		
+ 8 minutes		
+ 10 minutes		

6. Graph your results in the space below.

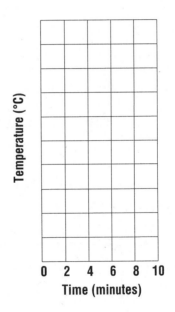

7. Hypothesis: <u>Sample hypothesis: The effect of global warming will be greater in dry regions than in humid regions.</u>

8. Record your experimental design on a separate sheet of paper.

9. Prediction: <u>Sample prediction: I predict that the temperature of dry soil in a covered jar will increase more rapidly than the temperature of wet soil in a covered jar when both jars are placed in sunlight.</u>

11. Record your data in the table. Use a separate sheet of paper for additional data if needed.

Time	Temperature	
	Jar 1: _____	Jar 2: _____
Before going outdoors	Data will vary.	
When first placed in sun		
+ 2 minutes		
+ 4 minutes		
+ 6 minutes		
+ 8 minutes		
+ 10 minutes		

12. Graph your results on a separate piece of paper.

13. Did your results agree with your predictions? __Answers will vary. Student answers should provide a clear__ __and precise interpretation of the results.__

What can you conclude? __Sample conclusion: The dry soil became warmer than the wet soil. Therefore, I can__ __conclude that my hypothesis is valid.__

14. Which variables had the greatest influence? __Answers will vary. Students will probably find that moisture,__ __darkness or lightness of surfaces, and thermal inertia (in the form of ice) all significantly affect the rate of__ __greenhouse warming.__

Which had the least influence? _____

15. How did your experiment model differences in global warming rates? __Sample answer: My experiment__ __reflects the likelihood that arid regions would be more affected by global warming than would humid regions.__

How did your model differ from the real world? __The experimental model is very simplistic and does not__ __account for the interaction between arid and non-arid regions. Furthermore, few regions will have soil as__ __moist as that in the model.__

TEXT INVESTIGATION 8

MINING FOR PEANUTS

2. Number of peanuts deposited: ___Students should deposit between 5 and 10 peanuts.___

In the space below, make a sketch of how the peanuts were distributed.

Sketches should be accurate and precise.

6. In the space below, sketch your completed landscape.

Sketches should be accurate and precise.

9. Number of peanuts you extracted: ___Accept all reasonable answers.___

10. How badly was the land damaged? ___Student answers should be clear and concise and should reflect a___ thorough investigation of the site. _____

How many peanuts were unearthed? _____

How many were buried? _____

How did number and distribution of peanuts affect mining results? _____

_____

How much waste was produced? _____

_____

Other observations: _____

_____

12. How hard was it to restore the site? ___Student answers should be clear and concise.___

_____

How closely does the reclaimed site resemble the original site? _____

_____

13. How does this simulation compare to actual mining operations? ___Generally, students will dig individual___ holes to extract nuggets of ore. In real practice, however, a company either would use strip-mining techniques or would bore shafts into the mineral deposit. _____

_____

14. How expensive do you think reclamation activities are compared with extracting the ore? ___The cost of___ reclamation could conceivably surpass the cost of the mining operation itself. _____

15. Did all the mining companies recover the same amount of minerals? ___Probably not___ If not, what accounted for the differences? ___The "miners" from some companies were probably faster,___ more skilled, or less concerned about damage to the land than others, or their sites may have contained more "ore."

16. What guidelines would you give to new miners to reduce environmental harm? ___Answers will vary.___ Students may suggest that the miners carefully document the state of the land before they mine, work slowly and carefully, and plan every step of the operation in advance.

T E X T   I N V E S T I G A T I O N **9**

THE CASE OF
THE FAILING FARM

5. What happens as water is sprayed onto the land? The soil washes down the slopes.

_____

6. Why are the streams becoming wider and shallower? The bottom of the stream fills with soil, and the

displaced water spreads over the banks to form a wider and shallower stream.

_____

7. What is the effect of the "cow tracks"? The fork loosens the soil, causing it to erode faster.

_____

_____

8. What happens if you cut the alfalfa? Erosion increases because the alfalfa no longer holds the soil in place.

_____

_____

9. Record the effect of the following modifications. If necessary, use a separate sheet of paper to describe the modification in more detail.

Planting corn and potato rows in different directions: Answers will vary, but students should notice that all

modifications could help lessen erosion if properly implemented.

_____

Exchanging alfalfa and corn crop locations: _____

_____

_____

Adding materials to soil: _____

_____

_____

Placing carpet in stream bed: _____

_____

_____

10. Note the effects of three other ideas for slowing erosion.

Idea 1: ___Answers will vary. For suggestions on experimental modifications, see Teaching Strategies for___

___Investigation on page T100.___

Effect: _____

_____

Idea 2: _____

_____

Effect: _____

_____

Idea 3: _____

_____

Effect: _____

_____

11. List five suggestions for preventing erosion on the Katawa farm.

(1) ___Sample answer: Avoid overgrazing.___

_____

(2) ___Sample answer: Rotate the crops.___

_____

(3) ___Sample answer: Plant windbreaks.___

_____

(4) ___Sample answer: Terrace the crops.___

_____

(5) ___Sample answer: Plant crops in rows that follow the contours of the land.___

_____

T E X T   I N V E S T I G A T I O N   10

BACKYARD DIVERSITY

3. Record features of your sites in Table A.

Table A		
Feature	**Site 1**	**Site 2**
Maintenance	**Data will vary.**	
Time left undisturbed		
Sunlight exposure		
Soil		
Rain		
Slope		
Water drainage		
Vegetation cover		

5. Record your observations in Table B.

Table B		
	Site 1	**Site 2**
Number of insects	**Data will vary.**	
Number of insect types		
Additional observations		

7. Best guess about reasons for differences between sites: __Answers will vary but should be clear and logical.__

_____

8. Hypothesis: __Sample hypothesis: Watering an area increases the number and diversity of insects found there.__

_____

9. Describe an experiment to test your hypothesis. __Sample description: I would find two sites of equal size,__ similar terrain, similar vegetation, similar sunlight exposure, etc., keeping all these variables constant. Then I would sample the two sites for insect number and diversity, using methods similar to those used in the Investigation. Assuming that the two sites were comparable in insect number and diversity, I would carry out the experiment by watering one site on a regular basis and not watering the other. After a specified period of time, say three months, I would sample the two sites again. If the watered site had a significantly greater number and diversity of insects than the unwatered site, I could conclude that my hypothesis was supported by the data. If there was no significant difference, or if the unwatered site had a greater number and diversity of insects, then I could conclude that my hypothesis was not supported by the data.

_____

T E X T   I N V E S T I G A T I O N   11

SOLAR DESIGN

3. Record temperatures in the table.

Time	Start	5 min.	10 min.	15 min.	20 min.	25 min.	30 min.
Temperature (°C)							

4. Hypothesis: ___Answers will vary but should be clear and logical._____

_____

5. Describe or sketch your new model design below:

Sample design, using sample hypothesis given in the textbook for item 4: Construct two houses that are identical except that one has smaller windows on the side facing the sun. Expose each house to exactly the same conditions, and measure the temperature of the interior of each house after a fixed period of time. If the temperature is greater in the house with larger windows, conclude that the data supported the hypothesis. If the temperature does not vary or is lower in the house with larger windows, conclude that the data did not support the hypothesis.

6. Record your results in the table.

Time	Start	5 min.	10 min.	15 min.	20 min.	25 min.	30 min.
Temperature (°C)							

7. Did your second model reach a higher temperature than your first model? **Answers will vary.**

_____

How do you account for the difference? **Answers will vary but should represent a logical interpretation of**

the results.

_____

_____

_____

8. How did more efficient designs differ from your design? **Answers will vary but should represent a logical**

interpretation of the results.

_____

_____

_____

_____

_____

_____

How would you redesign your model? **Answers will vary but should represent a logical interpretation of the**

results.

_____

_____

_____

_____

_____

_____

_____

9. If a passive solar heating system adds $5,000 to home construction costs, costs $25 per year to maintain, and saves $2,475 per year in heating costs, how long will it take for the solar heating system to pay for itself?

10 years

_____

T E X T   I N V E S T I G A T I O N   12

DOES FAST FOOD HAVE TO BE WASTEFUL?

3. Notes about how food is packaged:

Materials used: ___**Answers will vary, but student observations should be clear and complete.**___

_____

_____

Layers of packaging: _____

_____

_____

Utensils, condiments, and napkins: _____

_____

_____

Other observations: _____

_____

_____

_____

4. Number of people depositing trash in 30 minutes: ___**Answers will vary.**___

Notes about what is thrown away: _____

_____

_____

5. Estimated number of customers per day:

_____ × 2 × _____ × _____ × 2 = _____

People at one trash can   Hours per day   Number of trash cans

Notes: _____

_____

6. Estimated waste per customer: ___**Answers will vary.**___

_____

Estimated total daily waste: _____

_____

7. Are recycling containers provided? __Answers will vary, but useful data will depend on careful and thorough__

observations._____

Are they clearly labeled? _____

_____

Are customers following recycling instructions? _____

_____

8. Make notes for your report to Ms. Fairweather here, and then write your report on a separate sheet of paper.

General findings: __Answers will vary depending on specific circumstances. Reports should be clear, concise,__

and complete._____

_____

_____

_____

Ways to avoid producing waste: _____

_____

_____

_____

Ways to replace disposable items with reusable ones: _____

_____

_____

_____

Waste items that could be recycled or composted: _____

_____

_____

_____

Ways to replace nonrecyclable, noncompostable items: _____

_____

_____

_____

TEXT INVESTIGATION 13

WHAT CAUSES A
POPULATION EXPLOSION?

2. Make an age-structure histogram below.

Age-Structure Histogram for 1995

Age	Males	Females
75–79		
70–74		
65–69		
60–64		
55–59		
50–54		
45–49		
40–44		
35–39		
30–34		
25–29		
20–24		
15–19		
10–14		
5–9		
0–4		

5,000   0   5,000

Population

3.–6. Record the results of your calculations in the table on the next page.

7. Graph the total population below.
   Answers can be found on page 159.

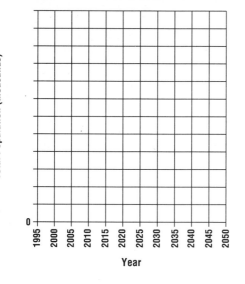

Total Population (thousands)

1995 2000 2005 2010 2015 2020 2025 2030 2035 2040 2045 2050

Year

8. Make an age-structure histogram below.

Age-Structure Histogram for 2050

Age	Males	Females
75–79		
70–74		
65–69		
60–64		
55–59		
50–54		
45–49		
40–44		
35–39		
30–34		
25–29		
20–24		
15–19		
10–14		
5–9		
0–4		

0

Population

Answers can be found on page 159.

9. Which factor had a greater effect on population growth?

The number of children per woman had a

greater effect on population growth.

10. Did any of the graphs show no growth in population? Explain these results.

No. Even if people choose to have only one or

two children, there are still so many people

having children that the population will

continue to increase. However, the growth of

populations with only two children per family

will taper off as the number of women of

childbearing age stabilizes.

TEXT INVESTIGATION, CONTINUED

Data shown are for Group A (top row) and Group B (bottom row). See page T136 for Groups C and D answers.

Year

Age	1995	2000	2005	2010	2015	2020	2025	2030	2035	2040	2045	2050
75–79	500 / 500	600 / 600	700 / 700	800 / 800	900 / 900	1,000 / 1,000	1,250 / 1,250	1,500 / 1,500	2,000 / 2,000	2,500 / 2,500	3,000 / 3,000	4,000 / 4,000
70–74	600 / 600	700 / 700	800 / 800	900 / 900	1,000 / 1,000	1,250 / 1,250	1,500 / 1,500	2,000 / 2,000	2,500 / 2,500	3,000 / 3,000	4,000 / 4,000	5,000 / 5,000
65–69	700 / 700	800 / 800	900 / 900	1,000 / 1,000	1,250 / 1,250	1,500 / 1,500	2,000 / 2,000	2,500 / 2,500	3,000 / 3,000	4,000 / 4,000	5,000 / 5,000	6,500 / 6,500
60–64	800 / 800	900 / 900	1,000 / 1,000	1,250 / 1,250	1,500 / 1,500	2,000 / 2,000	2,500 / 2,500	3,000 / 3,000	4,000 / 4,000	5,000 / 5,000	6,500 / 6,500	8,000 / 8,000
55–59	900 / 900	1,000 / 1,000	1,250 / 1,250	1,500 / 1,500	2,000 / 2,000	2,500 / 2,500	3,000 / 3,000	4,000 / 4,000	5,000 / 5,000	6,500 / 6,500	8,000 / 8,000	10,000 / 10,000
50–54	1,000 / 1,000	1,250 / 1,250	1,500 / 1,500	2,000 / 2,000	2,500 / 2,500	3,000 / 3,000	4,000 / 4,000	5,000 / 5,000	6,500 / 6,500	8,000 / 8,000	10,000 / 10,000	12,500 / 7,500
45–49	1,250 / 1,250	1,500 / 1,500	2,000 / 2,000	2,500 / 2,500	3,000 / 3,000	4,000 / 4,000	5,000 / 5,000	6,500 / 6,500	8,000 / 8,000	10,000 / 10,000	12,500 / 7,500	16,250 / 10,000
40–44	1,500 / 1,500	2,000 / 2,000	2,500 / 2,500	3,000 / 3,000	4,000 / 4,000	5,000 / 5,000	6,500 / 6,500	8,000 / 8,000	10,000 / 10,000	12,500 / 7,500	16,250 / 10,000	20,000 / 12,500
35–39	2,000 / 2,000	2,500 / 2,500	3,000 / 3,000	4,000 / 4,000	5,000 / 5,000	6,500 / 6,500	8,000 / 8,000	10,000 / 10,000	12,500 / 7,500	16,250 / 10,000	20,000 / 12,500	25,000 / 16,250
30–34	2,500 / 2,500	3,000 / 3,000	4,000 / 4,000	5,000 / 5,000	6,500 / 6,500	8,000 / 8,000	10,000 / 10,000	12,500 / 7,500	16,250 / 10,000	20,000 / 12,500	25,000 / 16,250	31,250 / 20,000
25–29	3,000 / 3,000	4,000 / 4,000	5,000 / 5,000	6,500 / 6,500	8,000 / 8,000	10,000 / 10,000	12,500 / 7,500	16,250 / 10,000	20,000 / 12,500	25,000 / 16,250	31,250 / 20,000	40,625 / 25,000
20–24	4,000 / 4,000	5,000 / 5,000	6,500 / 6,500	8,000 / 8,000	10,000 / 10,000	12,500 / 7,500	16,250 / 10,000	20,000 / 12,500	25,000 / 16,250	31,250 / 20,000	40,625 / 25,000	50,000 / 18,750
15–19	5,000 / 5,000	6,500 / 6,500	8,000 / 8,000	10,000 / 10,000	12,500 / 7,500	16,250 / 10,000	20,000 / 12,500	25,000 / 16,250	31,250 / 20,000	40,625 / 25,000	50,000 / 18,750	62,500 / 25,000
10–14	6,500 / 6,500	8,000 / 8,000	10,000 / 10,000	12,500 / 7,500	16,250 / 10,000	20,000 / 12,500	25,000 / 16,250	31,250 / 20,000	40,625 / 25,000	50,000 / 18,750	62,500 / 25,000	78,125 / 31,250
5–9	8,000 / 8,000	10,000 / 10,000	12,500 / 7,500	16,250 / 10,000	20,000 / 12,500	25,000 / 16,250	31,250 / 20,000	40,625 / 25,000	50,000 / 18,750	62,500 / 25,000	78,125 / 31,250	101,562 / 40,625
0–4	10,000 / 10,000	12,500 / 7,500	16,250 / 10,000	20,000 / 12,500	25,000 / 16,250	31,250 / 20,000	40,625 / 25,000	50,000 / 18,750	62,500 / 25,000	78,125 / 31,250	101,562 / 40,625	125,000 / 50,000
Total	48,250 / 48,250	60,250 / 55,250	75,900 / 64,650	95,200 / 76,450	119,400 / 91,900	149,750 / 111,000	189,375 / 135,000	238,125 / 152,500	299,125 / 176,000	375,250 / 205,250	474,312 / 243,375	596,312 / 290,375

WHAT CAUSES A POPULATION EXPLOSION?

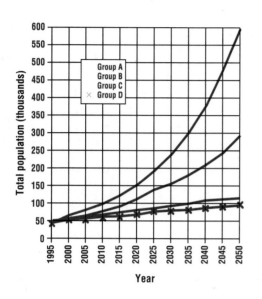

8.

Group A Age-Structure Histogram for 2050

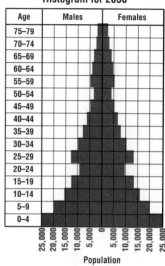

Group B Age-Structure Histogram for 2050

Group C Age-Structure Histogram for 2050

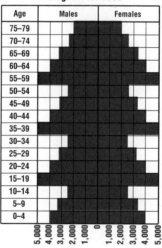

Group D Age-Structure Histogram for 2050

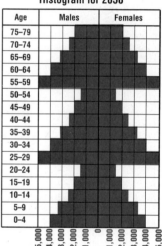

Data shown are for Group C (top row) and Group D (bottom row).

Age	1995	2000	2005	2010	2015	2020	2025	2030	2035	2040	2045	2050
75–79	500 / 500	600 / 600	700 / 700	800 / 800	900 / 900	1,000 / 1,000	1,250 / 1,250	1,500 / 1,500	2,000 / 2,000	2,500 / 2,500	3,000 / 3,000	4,000 / 4,000
70–74	600 / 600	700 / 700	800 / 800	900 / 900	1,000 / 1,000	1,250 / 1,250	1,500 / 1,500	2,000 / 2,000	2,500 / 2,500	3,000 / 3,000	4,000 / 4,000	5,000 / 5,000
65–69	700 / 700	800 / 800	900 / 900	1,000 / 1,000	1,250 / 1,250	1,500 / 1,500	2,000 / 2,000	2,500 / 2,500	3,000 / 3,000	4,000 / 4,000	5,000 / 5,000	6,500 / 6,500
60–64	800 / 800	900 / 900	1,000 / 1,000	1,250 / 1,250	1,500 / 1,500	2,000 / 2,000	2,500 / 2,500	3,000 / 3,000	4,000 / 4,000	5,000 / 5,000	6,500 / 6,500	8,000 / 8,000
55–59	900 / 900	1,000 / 1,000	1,250 / 1,250	1,500 / 1,500	2,000 / 2,000	2,500 / 2,500	3,000 / 3,000	4,000 / 4,000	5,000 / 5,000	6,500 / 6,500	8,000 / 8,000	10,000 / 10,000
50–54	1,000 / 1,000	1,250 / 1,250	1,500 / 1,500	2,000 / 2,000	2,500 / 2,500	3,000 / 3,000	4,000 / 4,000	5,000 / 5,000	6,500 / 6,500	8,000 / 8,000	10,000 / 10,000	5,000 / 3,000
45–49	1,250 / 1,250	1,500 / 1,500	2,000 / 2,000	2,500 / 2,500	3,000 / 3,000	4,000 / 4,000	5,000 / 5,000	6,500 / 6,500	8,000 / 8,000	10,000 / 10,000	5,000 / 3,000	6,500 / 4,000
40–44	1,500 / 1,500	2,000 / 2,000	2,500 / 2,500	3,000 / 3,000	4,000 / 4,000	5,000 / 5,000	6,500 / 6,500	8,000 / 8,000	10,000 / 10,000	5,000 / 3,000	6,500 / 4,000	8,000 / 5,000
35–39	2,000 / 2,000	2,500 / 2,500	3,000 / 3,000	4,000 / 4,000	5,000 / 5,000	6,500 / 6,500	8,000 / 8,000	10,000 / 10,000	5,000 / 3,000	6,500 / 4,000	8,000 / 5,000	10,000 / 6,500
30–34	2,500 / 2,500	3,000 / 3,000	4,000 / 4,000	5,000 / 5,000	6,500 / 6,500	8,000 / 8,000	10,000 / 10,000	5,000 / 3,000	6,500 / 4,000	8,000 / 5,000	10,000 / 6,500	5,000 / 8,000
25–29	3,000 / 3,000	4,000 / 4,000	5,000 / 5,000	6,500 / 6,500	8,000 / 8,000	10,000 / 10,000	5,000 / 3,000	6,500 / 4,000	8,0000 / 5,000	10,000 / 6,500	5,000 / 8,000	6,500 / 10,000
20–24	4,000 / 4,000	5,000 / 5,000	6,500 / 6,500	8,000 / 8,000	10,000 / 10,000	5,000 / 3,000	6,500 / 4,000	8,000 / 5,000	10,000 / 6,500	5,000 / 8,000	6,500 / 10,000	8,000 / 3,000
15–19	5,000 / 5,000	6,500 / 6,500	8,000 / 8,000	10,000 / 10,000	5,000 / 3,000	6,500 / 4,000	8,000 / 5,000	10,000 / 6,500	5,000 / 8,000	6,500 / 10,000	8,000 / 3,000	10,000 / 4,000
10–14	6,500 / 6,500	8,000 / 8,000	10,000 / 10,000	5,000 / 3,000	6,500 / 4,000	8,000 / 5,000	10,000 / 6,500	5,000 / 8,000	6,500 / 10,000	8,000 / 3,000	10,000 / 4,000	5,000 / 5,000
5–9	8,000 / 8,000	10,000 / 10,000	5,000 / 3,000	6,500 / 4,000	8,000 / 5,000	10,000 / 6,500	5,000 / 8,000	6,500 / 10,000	8,000 / 3,000	10,000 / 4,000	5,000 / 5,000	6,500 / 6,500
0–4	10,000 / 10,000	5,000 / 3,000	6,500 / 4,000	8,000 / 5,000	10,000 / 6,500	5,000 / 8,000	6,500 / 10,000	8,000 / 3,000	10,000 / 4,000	5,000 / 5,000	6,500 / 6,500	8,000 / 8,000
Total	48,250 / 48,250	52,750 / 50,750	58,650 / 54,150	65,950 / 58,450	75,150 / 64,150	79,250 / 71,250	84,750 / 80,250	91,500 / 82,000	100,000 / 84,500	103,000 / 87,500	107,000 / 91,500	112,000 / 96,500

(Year)

T E X T   I N V E S T I G A T I O N

BE AN ENVIRONMENTAL JOURNALIST

1. Make notes about relevant articles here, continuing on a separate sheet of paper as needed.

Article: _____

Summary: _____

_____

_____

Article: _____

Summary: _____

_____

_____

_____

Article: _____

Summary: _____

_____

_____

_____

Article: _____

Summary: _____

_____

_____

2. Issue chosen:_____

3. Copy the form on the next page to record information about each source you use.

How can the way that an issue is reported affect public opinion about it? _____

_____

4. Write your article on a separate sheet of paper.

5. How do your classmates' opinions compare with yours? _____

_____

RESEARCH SUMMARY FORM

Title: _____

Author: _____

Source: _____ Date: _____

Type of source: _____

Side(s) presented: _____

_____

Main points made: _____

_____

_____

_____

_____

_____

_____

_____

Conflicting information: _____

_____

_____

Flaws in logic: _____

_____

_____

Biases: _____

_____

_____

Other notes: _____

_____

_____

_____

MASTER MATERIALS LIST

The following items are used only for Investigations appearing in the *Laboratory Guide.* The Master Materials List for the textbook Investigations appears on pages T25–T26 of the textbook.

Material (Investigation no.)	Quantity per group
acrylic sheets, 3 cm × 5 cm (7.3)	5
aerial photos (8.1)	2
air popper (13.2)	1
air popper measuring cup (13.2)	1
all-purpose cleaner (12.2)	1 container
almanac or statistical census abstract (13.1)	1
aluminum foil (2.2, 5.2*)	several sheets
ammonia (12.2)	1 small bottle
aquarium, 15 gal., with cover (7.1)	1
aquarium gravel, light-colored (9.2)	several handfuls
baking sheet (7.3)	1
baking soda (12.2)	1 small package
balance, metric (9.1)	1
beakers, 50 mL (3.2, 6.2)	3
100 mL (1.1, 3.2, 13.1)	3
150 mL (2.2)	1
250 mL (9.1)	1
400 mL (1.1)	3
500 mL (9.2)	1
small (5.2)	1
black paper (4.3)	several sheets
bleach (10.1*, 12.2)	1 small bottle
borax (12.2)	1 small package
bowls (13.2)	15
bran flakes (2.2)	1 small box
calculator (8.1)	1 per student
scientific (13.1)	1
candles, 4–6 in. long (11.2)	1
cans, smaller than coffee cans (11.1)	1
capillary pipet (13.1)	1
cardboard (11.1*)	several pieces
cellophane tape (2.2)	1 roll
cellulose insulation (11.1*)	several pieces

Material (Investigation no.)	Quantity per group
cereal, sweet (2.2)	1 small box
cereal boxes (4.3)	4 per student
chalk (12.2)	a few pieces
clay (11.2)	1 small ball
clock (1.1, 5.2, 9.1)	1
cloth, pieces (5.2*)	several
thick (11.1*)	several pieces
coffee can with lid (11.1)	1
coffee filters (5.2*)	several
colored pencils (3.3, 7.2, 8.1, 10.2, 12.1)	an assortment
compost (9.1*)	5 g
computer or graphing calculator (13.2)	1
construction paper, dark (or a dark cloth) (7.3)	several sheets
containers for water, shallow (5.2)	2
1 L, clear (10.1)	1
corn flakes (2.2)	1 small box
corn syrup (1.1)	about 50 mL
cotton balls (5.2*)	a handful
cotton batting (11.1*)	several pieces
cotton swabs (7.3)	5
cow manure (9.1*)	5 g
craft knives, large (12.1)	2
craft sticks (5.2*)	several
cream of tartar (12.2)	1 small container
crucible (9.1)	1
delivery tubes, rubber or plastic (1.1)	3
desk lamps with an adjustable beam (2.2†)	1
detergent, liquid* (5.2)	about 50 mL
dip net (5.2*)	1
disposable gloves (3.1)	1 pair per student
dissecting pan (2.2)	1
dowel (3.3)	1
drain opener (12.2)	1 small bottle

* *One of several possible materials for this activity*

† *Optional item for this activity*

dropper pipets (6.1).........................1 per student

egg cartons (3.1)...........................1 per student

egg yolk, hard-boiled (3.3) 1/4

eggshells, crushed (3.3) 1/2

Erlenmeyer flasks (6.1) 1

eyedropper (5.1, 9.1, 10.1, 13.1) 1

feathers (5.2, 11.1*) ....a handful

fertilizer, household use (5.1) ....1 container

   fertilizer (10.1*)..........................1 g

fiberglass insulation (11.1*) ....several pieces

field guides of local animals and plants (10.2)........1

   pond life (5.1) 1

   small animal, with skull illustrations (3.1).........1

filter paper (4.2, 9.1, 10.1) ....several sheets

flour (9.1*) ....5 g

fluorescent lamp (5.1) 1

food coloring, red (9.2) ....1 container

funnel (3.3, 9.1, 10.1) 1

furniture polish (12.2) ....1 small bottle

garbage items such as food, paper, lawn clippings,
   paper clips, plastic bags (12.1) ....an assortment

gloves, laboratory (2.1, 2.2, 3.1, 3.3, 5.1, 6.2,
   10.1, 12.1, 12.2) ....1 pair per student

goggles, safety (6.1, 3.3, 5.1, 6.2, 7.1, 9.1,
   10.1, 11.1, 11.2, 12.1, 12.2, 13.1)..........1 pair per student

goose-neck lamps, 60 W bulbs (4.3) 3

   adjustable, 100 W bulbs (7.1) 1

graduated cylinder, 100 mL (5.1, 11.1, 13.1) 1

graph paper (1.1, 7.2, 13.2) ....several sheets

grass clippings, chopped (9.1*)..................a few handfuls

heat sources such as Bunsen burner, hot plate,
   or oven (9.1) 1

highlighter pen (8.1) ....1 per student

hot plate (11.1) 1

houseplants, potted, flowering (6.2).............2

ice cubes, large (7.1) 24

incense stick (7.1) 1

incubator (4.2) 1

index card (2.2) ....1 per student

jar (glass), 1 gal. with screw-on lid (11.2) 1

   1 qt. (5.1, 13.4) 3, 1

lab aprons (2.1, 2.2, 3.2, 3.3, 5.1, 5.2, 6.2, 10.1,
   11.2, 12.1) ....1 per student

laundry detergent (12.2) ....1 small container

laundry stain remover (12.2)...................1 small container

leaves, chopped (9.1*) ....a few handfuls

lemon, cut (12.2) 1

lemon juice (12.2).........................1 small bottle

lid for 1 L container (10.1*) 1

limewater (11.2)..........................about 200 mL

magnifying lenses (8.1) ....1 per student

marking pens (4.1, 9.3)......................an assortment

matches (7.1, 11.2) ....1 book

mealworms, live (2.2) 10

measuring cups (9.3, 12.2) 1

measuring spoons (9.3, 12.2)..................1

microscope (2.1, 5.2, 6.1, 10.1, 13.1) 1

microscope slides with coverslips (2.1,5.1,10.1,13.1) .. several

mitts, heatproof (11.1) ....1 pair

mixing bowl (12.2) 1

molasses (13.1) ....5 mL

nail polish, colored (13.4)....................2 shades

nails (11.1) 1

   large (12.1)............................1

newspaper (12.2) ....several sheets

   shredded (3.3) ....small handful

nylon scouring pad (12.2).....................1

nylon stocking (9.2).........................1 piece

   pieces (5.2*) ....a few pieces

oil, olive (12.2)...........................2 tbsp

   vegetable (5.2) ....100 mL

oven cleaner (12.2) ....1 small bottle

owl pellets (3.1) 1

paint, watercolor, solid, blue (9.2) 1

pan, 9 in. × 13 in. (5.2) 1

   shallow (12.1) 2

paper, white (2.2) ....several sheets

paper bags, brown, torn in pieces (5.2*)............1

paper cup (9.2)...........................1

paper towels (5.2*, 9.3, 10.1, 12.2) ....1 roll

pebbles (13.4) ....several handfuls

Petri dishes (4.1)..........................12

petroleum jelly (2.1) ....1 small jar

pH paper (6.1, 10.1)........................several sheets

pipe cleaners (5.2).........................several

plastic bags, large, clear (6.2) 2

   sealable (4.2, 9.3) ....several per student

plastic foam (5.2*) ....several pieces

   shredded (11.1*)........................several pieces

plastic soda bottles, clear with screw-top
   500 mL (3.3)...........................2

   3 L (9.2, 9.3, 12.1) 1, 4, 2

* One of several possible materials for this activity

† Optional item for this activity

Material (Investigation no.)	Quantity per group	Material (Investigation no.)	Quantity per group
plastic wrap, clear (4.3, 5.1, 5.2*)		stopwatches or watches that measure seconds (13.2)	1
popcorn kernels (13.2)	1 bag	straws, soda (5.2*, 6.1)	1 or 2; 1 per student
pots, small and soil† (9.3)	several	string (5.2*)	a few small pieces
protractor (4.3)	1 per student	sugar (3.2)	0.5 g per student
reference books (11.2)	an assortment	sulfuric acid, 1 M (6.2)	2 mL
rigid foam insulation (11.1*)	several pieces	sunscreens with four different SPF ratings (7.3)	1 small bottle of each
rock wool insulation (11.1*)	several pieces	sun-sensitive paper (7.3)	1 sheet
rubber band, small (9.2)	1	suntan lotion containing no sunscreen (7.3)	1 small bottle
ruler, metric (8.1)	1 per student	tape, masking (7.1, 9.3)	1 roll
(3.3, 10.2)	1	termites, live (2.1)	1 per student
saline solution (2.1)	a few drops	Terrasorb® granules* (9.1)	5 g
salt (3.2)	0.5 g	test tubes, 20 mm × 200 mm (1.1)	3
(9.3)	200 mL	thermometer, 12" alcohol (1.1, 4.3, 12.1)	1
sand (or gravel) (5.2, 11.1*, 12.1)	several handfuls	outdoor (7.1, 11.1)	2
light colored (9.2)	a few handfuls	toilet-bowl cleaner (12.2)	1 small container
saucepan or kettle (11.1)	1	tongs (9.1)	1 pair
sawdust* (5.2, 11.1, 9.1)		toothpicks (5.2*)	several
scissors (2.2, 4.3)	1 pair per student	topographic map (10.2)	1
seeds: alfalfa, clover, wild rye, wheat grass, and fescue (9.3)	10 of each	tracing paper (10.2)	1 sheet
shredded paper (11.1*)	several handfuls	transect grid, copy (4.2)	1 per student
sieve (3.3)	1	tweezers (2.1, 3.1)	1 pair per student
small paintbrush (2.2)	1 per student	twist ties (or tape) (6.2)	2
sodium nitrite (6.2)	2 g	variety of solutions from acid to base (6.1)	an assortment
soil (9.1, 12.1)	50 g, a few handfuls	various packaged products (12.3)	an assortment
from a natural area (3.3)	1,000 cu. cm	various seeds, at least two varieties (4.2)	an assortment
soiled household items to be cleaned (12.2)	an assortment	vermiculite (11.1*)	a few handfuls
spatula, metal (11.2)	1	vinegar, white (10.1*, 12.2)	1 small bottle
sphagnum moss, chopped (9.1*)	5 g	water (3.2, 7.3, 9.1, 9.2, 11.1, 13.1)	about 200 mL
sponge (12.2)	1 per student	distilled (5.1)	2.5 L
torn in pieces (5.2*)	a few pieces	fresh from a naturally occurring source (3.3)	about 1 L
spoon (3.3, 5.2, 12.2)	1 per student	from a pond containing viable organisms (5.1, 10.1)	about 1 L
spray bottle (12.1, 12.2)	1	wax pencils (3.3, 5.1, 7.3)	1
spray nozzle and tube from spray bottle (9.2)	1	window cleaner (12.2)	1 small bottle
stapler (9.3)	1 per student	wood fiber, decayed* (9.1)	5 g
steel wool (12.2)	1 piece	wood shavings* (5.2)	a few handfuls
stirring rod (5.1, 9.1, 10.1, 13.1)	1	wool* (11.1)	several pieces
stoppers, #2 one-hole (1.1)	3	yeast, baker's (1.1, 3.2, 6.1, 13.1)	1 package

* *One of several possible materials for this activity*

† *Optional item for this activity*